Stories from South Asia

selected and edited by
John Welch

Oxford University Press

Oxford University Press, Walton Street, Oxford OX2 6DP

Oxford New York Toronto
Delhi Bombay Calcutta Madras Karachi
Petaling Jaya Singapore Hong Kong Tokyo
Nairobi Dar es Salaam Cape Town
Melbourne Auckland

and associated companies in
Berlin Ibadan

Oxford is a trade mark of Oxford University Press

© Selection John Welch 1988

Second impression 1991

ISBN 0 19 831255 5

Commentary section written by John Welch and Andrew Goodwyn.

The publishers would like to thank the following for permission to
reproduce photographs.

Hulton Picture Library (p. 167 top and bottom, p. 168 top); MacQuitty
International Collection (p. 169 top right and bottom right); Network
(p. 169 middle right); ZEFA (p. 168 bottom right and left, p. 170 top and
bottom).

Cover illustration by Babu Xavier.
Courtesy of Victoria & Albert Museum.
Photograph by Philip de Bay.

Set by Pentacor Ltd, High Wycombe, Bucks
Printed in Hong Kong

Contents

Acknowledgements

The editor and publisher are grateful for permission to include copyright material in this anthology.

Mulk Raj Anand: from *Across the Black Waters*. Reprinted by permission of the author. **Iftikhar Arif:** 'The Twelfth Man' from *The Penguin Book of Modern Urdu Poetry* selected and translated by Mahmood Jamal (Penguin Books, 1986), copyright © Mahmood Jamal, 1986. Reprinted by permission of Penguin Books Ltd. **Bhibutibhushan Banerji:** extracts from *Pather Panchali* (1968), translated by T. W. Clarke. Reprinted by permission of Unwin Hyman Ltd. **Kamala Das:** 'An Introduction' from *The Old Playhouse* (1973). Reprinted by permission of Orient Longman Ltd, India. **Anita Desai:** 'Circus Cat Alley Cat'. Reprinted by permission of the author. **Shashi Deshpande:** from *Roots and Shadows* (1983). Reprinted by permission of Orient Longman Ltd., India. **Faiz Ahmad Faiz:** 'A Prison Nightfall' from *The Penguin Book of Modern Urdu Poetry* selected and translated by Mahmood Jamal (Penguin Books, 1986), copyright © Mahmood Jamal, 1986. **Mahatma Gandhi:** from *An Autobiography or The Story of My Experiments with Truth*. Copyright © Navajivan Trust, reprinted with their permission.

Sunil Gangopadhyay: from *Pratidwandi*, translated by Enakshi Chatterjee (1974). Reprinted by permission of Orient Longman Ltd., India. **Dawood Haider:** 'I Left You Behind' from *Take Me Home Rickshaw* (Salamander London, 1975), translated by Farida Majid. **Kaiser Haq:** 'Master Babu'. Reprinted by permission of the author. **Arun Joshi:** 'The Only American from our Village' from *Contemporary Indian English Short Stories*, edited by Madhusudan Prasad (Sterling Publ. PVT Ltd.). Reprinted by permission of the author. **Shekkar Joshi:** 'Big Brother' from *Modern Hindi Short Stories*, translated by Gordon Roadarmel. © 1972 The Regents of the University of California. Reprinted by permission of The University of California Press. **Lakshmi Kannan:** 'Muniyakka', originally published in *Truth Tales: Stories by Indian Women* (Kali for Women, 1967). Copyright © 1967 Lakshmi Kannan. Reprinted by permission of the author. **Arun Kolatkar:** 'Heart of Ruin', 'The Priest's Son', 'The Butterfly' and 'Hills' from *Jejuri* (1976). Copyright the author and reprinted by permission of Clearing House, Bombay on his behalf. **Vyankatesh Madgulkar:** from *The Village Had No Walls* (Asia Publishing House, Bombay, 1958), translated by S. D. Deshmukh. Reprinted by permission of the author and translator. **Vidya Niwas Misra:** 'Aranyani: Forest Spirit' and 'Winter' from *The Indian Poetic Tradition*, translated by Vidya Niwas Misra, Leonard Nathan and Sachchidananda Vatsayan. **Kishwar Naheed:** 'I Am Not That Woman' from *The Penguin Book of Modern Urdu Poetry* selected and translated by Mahmood Jamal (Penguin Books, 1986), copyright © Mahmood Jamal, 1986. Reprinted by permission of Penguin Books Ltd. **R. K. Narayan:** 'A Horse and Two Goats' from

A Horse and Two Goats (The Bodley Head, 1970). **Nirala:** 'Breaking Stones' from *A Season on the Earth* (Columbia University Press, 1976), translated by David Rubin. **R. Parthasarathy:** from *Rough Passage* (OUP, India 1977). Reprinted by permission. **Taufiq Rafat:** 'Arrival of the Monsoon' and 'Wedding in the Flood' from *Wordfall: Three Pakistani Poets* (OUP, Karachi 1975), edited by Kaleem Omar. **A. K. Ramanujan:** 'Of Mothers, among other things' and 'Self-Portrait' from *Selected Poems* (OUP, India 1976). Reprinted by permission. Nine Tamil poems *The Poems of Love and War*, translated by A. K. Ramanujan (Columbia/UNESCO 1985: India, Oxford University Press). Reprinted by permission of the translator. **Rabindranath Tagore:** 'Last Honey' from *Selected Poems of Rabindranath Tagore*, translated by William Radice (Penguin Books, 1985), translation copyright © William Radice, 1985. Reprinted by permission of Penguin Books Ltd.

I should like to express my gratitude to Andrew Goodwyn for his help with the Commentary section of this anthology, in particular the Ideas for writing.

In addition, there have been many people who have helped me to acquire the information and experience that have gone to the making of this book. My thanks go to colleagues, members of the Multicultural Development Service and others, in the London Borough of Waltham Forest. A previous publication, *A Teacher's Guide to South Asian Literature* (London Borough of Waltham Forest 1987), was the outcome of a year's secondment from the Borough to the Institute of Education. I should like to express my gratitude to fellow-members of the South Asian Literature Society. Special thanks should go to Ranjana Ash, Carla Contractor, Lakshmi Holmstrom, Geoff Manuel and Ralph Russell.   *John Welch*

Preface

This anthology contains five complete short stories, extracts from novels and one autobiography, and poems. It aims to give an indication of the wide range of literature from South Asia now available in English, whether written in English or in English translation. The aims of such an anthology are discussed by Peter Traves in his Introduction. The passages have been chosen for their literary quality and the selection is not intended to be illustrative; at the same time an attempt has been made to encompass a range of themes. Themes that recur include: the physical environment as reflected in the literature; the cultural heritage and contact between cultures; language, varieties of language, and some of the conflicts the issue of language gives rise to; the impact of British rule and the Independence struggle; the changing roles of women; social tradition and social change; village life and city life and the transition from one to the other.

A brief section at the head of each passage gives a context, in the case of extracts from novels, together with a bare minimum of information essential to a first reading.

The commentary at the back provides much fuller background details and notes, biographical information, and points to think about in connection with each piece. There are ideas for writing, of a variety of kinds, but with an overall balance between English and English Literature work. At the end of this section there is a series of assignments that range across the anthology as a whole. Students need not have read the complete anthology to be able to complete an assignment but the work suggestions should encourage them to draw on at least several suggested sources. Some of these assignments would be suitable for the 'wider reading' section of the GCSE Syllabus. The ideas for writing and assignments are not of course intended to replace material that might be designed by a teacher using the anthology, but simply to be helpful and to allow students to use the book independently. Finally, 'Sources and Further Reading' offers some suggestions for wider reading in the field of South Asian Literature.

John Welch

Introduction

Peter Traves
English adviser, London Borough of Waltham Forest

John Welch's anthology is one that should be enjoyed by anyone who has an interest in literature, offering, as it does, an excellent introduction to a rich literary heritage that stretches over three thousand years. It contains a wide variety of prose and poetry by South Asian* writers. Hopefully adult readers will take great pleasure from the poems, stories, and extracts presented here and will feel encouraged to undertake their own wider reading in South Asian literature.

However, this anthology was also designed to meet another and more specific need. Its compilation arose out of an acute awareness of the paucity of literature from South Asia available and suitable for use in our schools. In particular, very little has been produced for, and directed at, the older age group in secondary schools. There are few texts which might begin to introduce students to the remarkable variety and quality of this literature. Ranjana Ash's *Short Stories from India, Pakistan and Bangladesh* (Harrap, 1980) is a notable and honourable exception. In the past many teachers might have been reluctant to use an anthology like this, fearing to stray too far from the set texts of examination syllabuses. This should no longer be a real obstruction. GCSE courses have built on the best practice of some old CSE and GCE syllabuses. Schools and individual teachers have a great deal of freedom to construct their own lists of 'set texts'. Furthermore, the fact that a large part, often all, of the assessment is made on the basis of course work allows the

---

* South Asia is a term commonly used to describe the countries of India, Pakistan, Bangladesh, and Sri Lanka, as well as smaller territories such as Nepal and Bhutan. Sometimes alternative terms such as the Indian Subcontinent, or simply the Subcontinent are used.

pupils to respond to the literature in a great variety of forms. A book like *Stories from South Asia* could form an integral part of a fourth and fifth year programme of work in either English or English Literature. There would be material here for children of widely different levels of ability as well as for children from widely different social and cultural backgrounds.

In the sixth form the anthology could be used as a resource for Practical Criticism work. There are also A Level courses where schools have the power to select some of their own set texts and *Stories from South Asia* could well be one of them. However, perhaps its most valuable role might be to extend the reading of the students beyond the narrow confines of the set book list. A Level examiners often comment upon the obviously restricted reading of some candidates and of the added strength evident in the answers of those students who have read widely. *Stories from South Asia* is an anthology that should be available in every secondary school library. It should be there for students to browse through at their leisure, reading for their own enjoyment yet extending and deepening their awareness of the variety of literary forms and of the contrasts and continuities that exist between cultures.

The writers whose works feature here have all been published in the Subcontinent and some have also been published in Britain and America. However, apart from one or two, Anita Desai and R. K. Narayan for example, their writing tends to be little known in Britain and unreasonably neglected. It is probably fair to say that South Asian literature was better known in Britain, and treated more seriously, sixty or seventy years ago than it is today. This may be due in part to the remarkable reluctance to study literature in translation in British schools and universities. However, this cannot be a total answer as the reputations of most major European writers rests on readings of their translated work. There is no shortage of classic European texts in translation in our bookshops, and to a lesser extent, the literature of the Far East, Chinese poetry in particular, is readily available and reasonably widely read.

It is ironic that South Asian literature has suffered from a lack of serious interest in this country at the very time when a great deal of attention has been focused on literature set in that part of the world but written by white Britons. Most notable recently have been the novels of Paul Scott which were made into the television series *The Jewel in the Crown*. E. M. Forster's novel *A Passage to India* has been made into a successful and much-praised film and while *The Far Pavilions* may not have met with the same critical approval, both book and television version were an enormous financial success. These books and films concentrate on the European experience in the India of the British Empire. Along with other books like *The Siege of Krishnapur* by J. G. Farrell, they represent a significant literary achievement reflecting a particular experience, a specific point of view on the Indian Subcontinent. It is, however, a very limited point of view and is not a substitute for a very different literature reflecting a very different experience—the experience of South Asians over thousands of years which has found expression in their poetry and prose.

Many people may be surprised to learn how many South Asian writers have written, and in some cases continue to write, in English. In fact India now publishes more English language titles each year than any other country apart from the USA and Great Britain. Writing in English in the Subcontinent goes back at least two hundred years to the social reformer Rammohan Roy. The examples included in this anthology come mainly from the twentieth century. The novelist Mulk Raj Anand has some interesting things to say about his own decision to write in English. He describes how he made the acquaintance of Irish writers and intellectuals like W. B. Yeats, AE, and Lady Gregory in the 1920s, people who were seeking to forge a national Irish literature in English. They were a colonial people using the language of their old rulers, the English, but in such a way that it would be seen as part of an Irish culture. As part of this endeavour they often attempted to enrich their English with the spoken rhythms and idioms of the Irish peasantry. Anand felt encouraged by their example to write in English while attempting to reproduce the turns of phrase, forms of speech, and

3

imagery of his Indian peasant characters. Thus it was that two experiences of colonial oppression, though half a world apart, shared enough to produce parallel literary expressions. Anand writes: 'I never faltered in my belief that, in creative writing by Indians in the English language, the *echo* of one's mother tongue, or near mother tongue, is bound to be heard to a greater or lesser extent.'

Of course most of the literature written in South Asia is not written in English. However, English tends to be the language into which the various literatures are translated for wider domestic consumption. There are around fourteen major literary languages in South Asia and people may be proficient in only one of them but may also be able to read English. Consequently English functions as a sort of literary 'link-language'.

The earliest of the translations included in this anthology are pieces from the Sanskrit language and of these the most ancient is the *Rig-Veda*, parts of which were composed around 1000 C. This makes it older than the most ancient surviving European literature. That is a fact we need to bear in mind when considering the range and achievement of the South Asian literary tradition.

In the West people sometimes hold stereotyped images of Indian thought and culture. These images are based partly on versions of Hindu philosophy that have been popularized in Britain and America. In the 1970s groups like the Beatles presented India as the home of a spiritual quest for peace and tranquillity. Celebrities and ordinary people from the West visited India to study meditation. It is certainly true that the Subcontinent, and Hinduism in particular, does have a rich religious and spiritual culture and naturally this has found expression in literature. However, this image tends to be a superficial one that does not do justice to the depth and complexity of either the spiritual or secular history of South Asia. The Subcontinent has had a turbulent and varied political history and the social commitment of many modern writers is represented in much of the work in this anthology. The sharpness of the irony and the acuteness of social observation will come as a surprise to those expecting the impenetrable and enigmatic vagueness of the sub-Hindu texts that abounded in the psychedelic seventies.

Literature has a valuable role to play in dispelling stereotypes and providing insights into different societies and cultures. Hopefully this anthology will play its part in that struggle. The presence in our classrooms, towns, and cities of people from a South Asian background who are now making a major contribution to the life, culture, and economy of Britain gives far greater relevance to this issue. However, it must be emphasized that the literature reflected in this anthology has had to make its way first and foremost as literature, and not as writing that illustrates a theme or provides information, and it is writing that deserves to be read and enjoyed by people from all backgrounds. What is included here is inevitably only a glimpse of a rich and varied literature, and for those who wish to look further, there are many exciting discoveries in store.

Aranyani: Forest Spirit

Translated by Vidya Niwas Misra,
Leonard Nathan, and Sachchidananda Vatsayan

This poem has been translated from the Sanskrit and comes from the
Rig-Veda, one of the earliest collections of Indian poetry, some of it
going back to 1000 BC.

Aranyani, Aranyani, always shifting back and back,
Why do You turn away from the village? It couldn't be fear.

When distant cattle begin to low and the cricket responds,
It is as though Aranyani laughed far off among bells.

Was it She once glimpsed out there, or a shimmer of cows
   or some house?
She can shape from the dusk a secret movement of carts.

Her voice is like someone calling the herds, like a falling
   tree
As it rends, or, to those in the woods after dark, the
   remotest wail.

She will not hurt unless someone unkind comes close.
Her food is the fruit in there, and she moves or rests
   where she will.

Sweet with the scent of the dark, served without tilling
   the ground,
Mother of all wild things: now, I have sung You, Aranyani.

Nine Tamil Poems

Translated by A. K. Ramanujan

These nine poems were written originally in Tamil, a language of south India, and come from an anthology called the *Kuruntokai*, which was compiled between AD 100 and 300.

1 What She Said

Nowhere, not among the warriors at their festival,
nor with the girls dancing close in pairs,
nowhere did I see my lover.

I am a dancer;
my pride, my lover,
        —for love of him
            these conch-shell bangles slip
            from my wasting hands—
he's a dancer too.

Ātimantiyār

2 What He Said

Her arms have the beauty
of a gently moving bamboo.
Her eyes are full of peace.
She is faraway,
her place not easy to reach.

My heart is frantic
with haste,

a ploughman with a single ox
on land all wet
and ready for seed.

Ōrēruṟavaṉār

3 What She Said

Shall I charge like a bull
against this sleepy town,
or try beating it with sticks,
or cry wolf
till it is filled with cries
of Ah's and Oh's?

It knows nothing, and sleeps
through all my agony, my sleeplessness,
and the swirls of this swaying south wind.

Oh what shall I do
to this dump of a town!

Auvaiyar

4 What He Said

What could my mother be
to yours? What kin is my father
to yours anyway? And how
did you and I meet ever?
But in love our hearts are as red
earth and pouring rain:
mingled
beyond parting.

Cempulappeyaṉīrār

8

5 What She Said

Once: if an owl hooted on the hill,
if a male ape leaped and loped
out there on the jackfruit bough in our yard
my poor heart would melt for fear. But now
      in the difficult dark of night
      nothing can stay its wandering
      on the long sloping mountain-ways
      of his coming.

Kapilar

6 What Her Friend Said

The great city fell asleep
but we did not sleep.
Clearly we heard, all night,
from the hillock next to our house
the tender branches of the flower-clustered tree
with leaves like peacock feet
let fall
their blue-sapphire flowers.

Kollan Arici

7 What She Said to Her Girl-Friend

On beaches washed by seas
older than the earth,
in the groves filled with bird-cries,
on the banks shaded by a *punnai*
clustered with flowers,
              when we made love
my eyes saw him
and my ears heard him;

my arms grow beautiful
in the coupling
and grow lean
as they come away.
                              What shall I make of this?

                        Veṇmaṇippūti

8   What He Said

My love is a two-faced thief.
In the dead of night
she comes like the fragrance
of the Red-Speared Chieftain's forest hills,
to be one with me.

And then, she sheds the petals
of night's several flowers,
and does her hair again
with new perfumes and oils,
to be one with her family at dawn

with a stranger's different face.

                              Kapilar

9   What She Said

The rains, already old,
have brought new leaf upon the fields.
The grass spears are trimmed and blunted
by the deer.
The jasmine creeper is showing its buds
through their delicate calyx
like the laugh of a wildcat.

In jasmine country, it is evening
for the hovering bees,
but look, he hasn't come back.

He left me and went in search
of wealth.

Okkūr Mācātti

Pather Panchali

Bibhutibhushan Banerji
Translated by T. W. Clarke and Tarapada Mukherji

These two passages are taken from a novel written in Bengali which tells the story of Opu and his elder sister Durga, growing up in a village in Bengal in the early part of this century. Shorbojoya is their mother, and the *Mahabharat*, from which she recites in the first passage, is one of the two great epics of ancient India. It was composed at different times but reached its final form between 200 BC and AD 200, and tells the story of the struggle between the five sons of Pandu (the 'Pandavas') and the hundred sons of the blind king Dhrtarashtra (the 'Kurus'). Arjun was a warrior from the Pandavas and Karna, with whom Opu so passionately identifies, was one of the heroes of the Kurus. The 'teacher Dron' was originally tutor to the Pandavas but later became the chief general of the Kurus.

1

One day, as she often did after their midday meal, Shorbojoya lay down by the window, spread her sari around her, and began to chant part of the *Mahabharat* from a tattered copy of the poem by Kasidas. A fish hawk called from the coconut tree at the side of the house, and Opu, who was seated by her side, was writing his a b c, and listening to her as she sang. Suddenly she broke off and called out to Durga. 'Durga, get me some betel.' Opu wanted her to go on. 'Mummy, what about the story of the girl who collected cow-dung?'

'The story of the girl and the cow-dung, you say? Oh, you mean that story of Hari Hor's! It's not in this book; it's in the *Annadamangal*.'

By this time she had the betel in her mouth and went droning on.

> The king said, 'Hear me while I tell
> A wondrous tale, which mark you well,
> Of King Somadutt who lived in Sind,
> A foe alike of gods . . .'

At this point Opu interrupted her. He held his hand up to her mouth and asked for a bit of the betel she was chewing. She took some of it out of her mouth and put it into his outstretched hand. 'Be careful though,' she said, 'It's very bitter. It's the *khoyer* bark. I tell your father every day not to buy this kind of bark, but still . . .'

Opu was not listening. His eyes were fixed on the bamboos outside the window and on the criss-cross of light and shade they cast on the jungle bushes beneath. All he heard—he had ears for nothing else—was that story from the *Mahabharat*, the story of the battle of Kurukshetra, and in particular the part about Karna. Of all the characters in the *Mahabharat* he liked Karna best. He had a special sympathy for him: Karna with his chariot wheels stuck in the mud, making a superhuman effort to drag them clear; Karna, for the moment unarmed and alone, his hands busy with the chariot wheels, making his pathetic appeal to Arjun's chivalry. But alas, Arjun spurned his plea and struck him dead with a shaft from his bow. As he listened to his mother telling this part of the story Opu's young heart was stricken with grief, and there was no holding back the tears. They flooded out of his eyes and streamed down his soft delicate cheeks; but as he wept there was born in his mind a sympathetic insight he had not experienced before, and with it a feeling of happiness, happiness that comes of weeping for another's sorrow. There is a road through life which leads to compassion, compassion for the tears of man, compassion for his poverty, compassion for his pain, his hopelessness, his sense of frustration and his death; and the sign-posts which pointed the way for Opu were the midday sun, the musty smell which spread through the air from the torn pages of that old book, and the gentle music of his mother's

13

voice. Then as the day wore on, Shorbojoya returned to her housework and Opu went out and stood on the verandah, staring at the distant banyan tree. Sometimes the high branches were hazy in the shimmering heat of mid-summer; at other times they glowed red in the still light of the evening sun. More than anything else, it was the sight of the tree stained with the red colours of evening that filled his mind with grief; and in the far distance, beyond the banyan, where the sky leant down to the earth, he could see Karna, his hands labouring to drag the chariot wheels clear of the mud. Every day he laboured, every day, Karna, the mighty hero, the object of a pity which could never end. It was Arjun who won the kingdom; it was Arjun who won the fame; it was Arjun who slew his hapless foe with a bolt loosed from his chariot; but his was not the victory. Karna was the victor; Karna it was who lived on in the tears of countless generations, ever present where love is born of human pain.

Day after day Opu listened to the tales of the *Mahabharat* war, but there were not nearly enough battles for him. So to make good this deficiency he worked out a plan whereby he could revel in battles to his heart's content. He armed himself with a bamboo switch and a thin branch from a tree. Then he paced up and down the path, which led through the grove, or up and down the yard outside the house, and there he re-enacted the scenes for himself. First, Dron shot ten arrows. It could not have been fewer. And what did Arjun do? He fired off at least two hundred arrows. Then—oh!—what a battle there was; what a battle! There were so many arrows that the sky became dark with them. (Yet however many arrows his fancy launched, his imaginary battle did not outdo Kasidas's story of the *Mahabharat* war as he heard his mother sing it.) What did Arjun do next? He seized his shield and his sword and leapt down from the chariot. And how he fought! Duryadhan came, and then Bhim. Their arrows darkened the sky. You could not see a thing. But the battle in which the warriors of the *Mahabharat* won their fame lasted only eighteen days. If they had been alive today they would have realized that the path to glory had in the meantime become much more difficult. To satisfy the eager longings of a boy they would have had to ply their weapons for months on end without respite. Could even they have fought for so long?

It was a day in the hot weather, at the beginning of May. The scene was the edge of the jungle near Nilmoni Ray's house. It was just before noon. The teacher Dron was in great trouble. Arjun's chariot, the one with the monkey banner, had run over his shoulder. There was Arjun's bow, the Gandiva, and in it the fatal arrow which the god Brahma had given him. In a second it would be fired. The hosts of the Kurus, Dron's troops, had already raised a cry of alarm, when an amused voice called out from the jungle thickets behind him, 'What on earth are you up to, Opu?' Opu started and released the bow-string which was at that moment drawn right back to his ear. Then he looked round and saw his sister standing among the bushes laughing at him. 'You silly boy!' she said. 'What are you doing muttering to yourself and waving your arms and legs about?' Then affectionately, 'Silly! What a silly boy you are! What were you talking to yourself for?'

Opu flushed with embarrassment. He made several efforts to speak, but the words would not come. 'Oh . . . I . . . I . . . wasn't . . . talking to myself . . . You know . . . I . . .!'

Durga was very amused but presently she stopped laughing and taking Opu by the hand said, 'Come along with me,' and led him off into the wood. After they had gone a little way, she pointed ahead and said with a laugh, 'Can you see all those custard apples? Lots of them are ripe, you know. How do you think we can get them down?'

2

There was one piece of information which Opu had not passed on to anybody yet, not even to his sister.

One day at about noon he had opened a wooden chest which belonged to his father. He had done it very quietly and nobody had seen him. The chest was crammed with books, and it was in one of them that he had come across this amazing piece of information.

He knew it was about midday because the shadow of the bamboo clump was not lying across the yard in a long line between east and west—village folk still tell the time of day by the length of shadows of that ancient banyan tree which grows in the vast Shonadanga plain.

On this particular day his father was out. Opu went into the room, quietly closing the door behind him, and managed to open the wooden chest without being detected. He was very excited. He opened the books one by one, and turned over the pages to see whether there were any pictures to look at or a good story. One book had a title on the cover, *An Anthology of Ancient Philosophical Works*. He had not the slightest notion what the title meant or what the book was about, but the cover was faded and mottled like marble, and as he turned it back a swarm of silverfish darted all over the page and disappeared as fast as they could. Opu raised the book to his nose. It had a peculiar old smell. The pages were thick and dust-coloured, and he loved the smell of them. There was something about the smell which made him think of his father. He did not know why it did, but it did, always.

It was the book in the damaged board cover and the mottled marble jacket which attracted him most, so he hid it under his bolster and put all the other books back in the box. He read it when he was alone, and one day he came across an amazing statement. If somebody had told him about it he would have been astonished, so would anyone else; but this was not hearsay, it was in cold print. The writer was describing the properties of mercury. If you put some mercury in a vulture's egg and leave it in the sun for a few days, and then hold it in the mouth, you can fly high up in the sky.

Opu could not believe his eyes. He read the passage again and again.

He hid the book in his own broken box, and went outside to think; and the more he thought the more surprised he was.

He said to his sister, 'Didi, do you know where vultures build their nests?'

She did not know. So he asked the boys in the village, Shotu,

Nilu, Kinu, Potol, Nera, all of them. One of them said, 'Not anywhere here. They build at the top of big trees in the open country.' His mother was cross with him. 'Where have you been wandering to in this heat?' He moved into his room and pretended to lie down. He opened the book and found the place again. There it was! Astonishing! It was so easy to fly and yet nobody knew about it. Perhaps nobody had a copy of this book except his father. Or it might be that all this time nobody's eye except his own had lighted on this particular place in the book.

He thrust his nose into the book again, and smelt it. That same old smell! It never occurred to him to question the truth of what was written in such a book.

There was no problem about mercury. He knew that mercury was quicksilver, and that it was quicksilver that was used on the back of mirrors. There was a broken mirror in the house, and he would be able to get some from there. The problem was where to get vultures' eggs.

One day after their midday meal his sister called out to him. 'Come here, Opu. Come and see the fun.' She had saved a handful of rice from her meal and gone out to the bamboos near the back door. From there she called, 'Bhulo—o—o—o—'. She called once only and then stood in silence, looking at Opu with a smile on her face. Her smile seemed to say that the gate of an unknown fairy city was going to open before their very eyes. Suddenly a dog appeared from somewhere. Durga pointed, 'Look, he's come,' she said. 'Did you see where he came from?' And she giggled happily.

This business of feeding the dog was apparently a daily routine for her, and she got great pleasure from it. 'You call: there's nobody in sight. Everywhere's quiet,' she told herself. She put the rice down on the ground and stood with her eyes shut, but in her heart there was great excitement, as hope that he would come fought with the fear that he might not; and she always talked to herself about it. 'I don't suppose Bhulo will come today. I must watch to see where he comes from. He's probably not heard me.'

Then suddenly there was a noise in the bushes, and there in

17

the twinkling of an eye was Bhulo, panting hard, and tearing aside the leaves and creepers.

A shiver of excitement thrilled through Durga's body. Her eyes were bright with surprise and curiosity. She said to herself, 'He heard me all right. But where does he come from? Tomorrow I'll call softly and see if he hears me then.'

So every day at mealtimes, in spite of her mother's scolding, she saved a little of her food to feed the dog with. It was such fun; and she did enjoy doing it.

Opu however could not see what fun there was in calling a dog. It was one of Durga's girl's games, and he was not interested. It gave him no particular pleasure to see a hungry dog eating his food. Besides, he had something else on his mind, vultures' eggs.

At last he got on to the track of them. The cowherd boys used to tie their cattle to the jackfruit tree that belonged to Hiru the barber, and go into the village to get oil and tobacco. Opu knew one of them. He lived in their part of the village. So he broached his problem to him. 'You go all over the countryside. Have you ever seen a vulture's nest? If you can get me some vultures' eggs I'll give you two pice.'

A few days later the cowherd boy turned up at the house and called Opu. When he came out he produced two small black eggs from a bag in his waistband. 'Look at what I've brought for you, sir,' he said—it was usual for low caste people to use the word 'sir' when addressing a brahmin—Opu stretched out an eager hand to take them. He turned them this way and that in high glee, and murmured, 'Vultures' eggs!' Then he said to the boy, 'They are real, aren't they?' The boy produced his evidence. It was most impressive! 'They must be vultures' eggs. There's no doubt about that. I got them from the top branch of a very high tree, and a very risky job it was too. But,' he added, 'I can't let you have them for less than two annas.'

Opu's face fell when he heard how much they would cost. 'I'll give you two pice,' he said, 'and you can have my cowries. I'll let you have all of them, and the tin box I keep them in. There are lots of golden coloured ones. Shall I show them to you?'

The cowherd boy was, it seemed, much more experienced in worldly matters than Opu. He was not prepared to sell the eggs except for cash. He haggled for a long time and eventually the price was fixed at four pice. Opu managed to get two pice from his sister, and completed the deal. Then he got the eggs, but the cowherd took some of his cowries as well. These cowries were Opu's life. At any other time he would not have parted with them for half a kingdom and a princess thrown in. But playing with cowries seemed poor sport in comparison with flying in the sky.

He had the eggs in his hand and his mind felt as light as a balloon when it is first blown up. Then slowly a little shadow of doubt rose in his mind to darken his joy. So far he had been quite sure; but once he had really got the eggs in his hand, he began to wonder. It was not a serious doubt however, just a suspicion of uncertainty. That evening before dark he was in Nera's orchard, sitting on a branch that had been cut off a rose-apple tree. His mind was busy with questions. 'Shall I really be able to fly now? Where shall I fly to? To my uncle's house? or to where Daddy has gone to? or shall I fly across the river? or shall I fly to where the stars rise in the sky, as the sparrows or the mynas do? Shall I do it today or tomorrow?'

Later that same evening Durga was looking for an old piece of cloth to use as a wick. While she was rummaging among some torn rags which were bundled together between the pots and pans, something rolled from the back of the shelf and fell on to the floor. It was dark indoors, and she could not see clearly, so she picked it up and took it outside to see what it was. 'Goodness, Mummy,' she exclaimed, 'there are two big eggs here. They've fallen and smashed. I wonder what bird came into the house and laid its eggs here.'

It is best to pass over what happened later on. Opu refused to touch his food for a whole day. He cried and made a terrific to-do. Shorbojoya talked about it when she went down to the pond for her bath. 'Opu's making an enormous fuss. I've never heard the like of it. Do you know, Shejbou? He says that if you have a vulture's egg you can fly. That cowherd boy's a proper scoundrel. He collected a couple of eggs from a crow's nest or somewhere, and said they were vultures' eggs. And he made Opu pay four pice for them. I can't tell you what a simpleton the lad is, Shejbou. I don't know what I'm going to do with him.'

How could the poor Shorbojoya know? Everybody had not read the *Anthology of Ancient Philosophical Works*, and not everybody knew the properties of mercury either.

It is as well they did not, because in that case everybody would be able to fly.

Winter   from the *Ramayana*

Translated by Vidya Niwas Misra,
Leonard Nathan, and Sachchidananda Vatsayan

These verses, describing the delights of winter, are translated from the
Sanskrit and come from the *Ramayana*, an epic ascribed to a date
between 400 and 200 BC.

The forests, swamped with mist and fringed
With fields of wheat and barley, gleam
As the sun rises and herons cry
And cranes, cheering the day's arrival.

The paddy is so rich with grain
Clustered like golden date-palm flowers,
It leans a little with their weight,
A field of weighty yellow light.

Rays trickling weakly down,
Buried in the cold and mist,
The sun, as though today it rose
From farther off, looks like the moon.

The morning sun hasn't attained
Its power; at noon its warmth is good
To feel, its hue the hue of cream,
Its presence cordial on the ground.

The country of the forest, just
As early sunlight slants across,
Touches those who see it, see
Its grasses lightly wet with dew.

The trees themselves, their flowers gone,
Seem to be sleeping now, lapped
In a shine of dew and swamped again
In the milky glimmer of the mist.

Its surface shadowed under haze,
Branches locked in the damp frost,
The river is lovely. Cranes in it
Are only known by crying out.

Even the water drop that hangs
From the leaf tip, is perfumed,
Having been born of frost, and born
Of gentle sun, and now so chill.

The lotus clusters, ruined by frost,
Are a bare thrust of black stalks
Whose leaves are shrivelled into age,
Whose saffron filament is crushed.

The ox, his eyes shut from fear
Of the bladed paddy ears, drinks
From the water standing in the field
Water warmed by his warm breath.

The wild elephant delights
To touch that chill and crystal water;
But, when he dips his trunk to drink,
He suddenly pulls it again.

Even these waterfowls, afloat
On the water's surface, at their ease,
Hesitate to dive below,
Like young men in their first war.

Last Honey

Rabindranath Tagore
Translated by William Radice

In this poem, translated from the Bengali, Tagore describes the season
of spring moving into summer. In Bengal, Caitra (mid-March to mid-
April) is the month of spring and the last month of the year. Baisakh
(mid-April to mid-May) marks the beginning of summer with its
oppressive heat and drought.

End of the year, of spring; wind, renouncing the world, leaves
   The empty harvested fields with a farewell call to the bees—

   Come, come; Caitra is going, shedding her leaves;
Earth spreads out her robe for summer languor beneath the
                                        trees;
But *sajne*-tresses dangle and mango-blossoms are not all shed,
   And edging the woods *ākanda* lays its welcoming bed.
   Come, come; in the drought there'll be nothing of these
But the dance of their withered wraiths in the barren night, so
                                   come, bees.

I hear the song of the closing year like a flute in the rustling
                                   leaves,
So smear your wings with pollen's chronicle before its fragrance
                                   flees.
   Take all you can from flowers that summer heat will strew;
   Cram the old year's honey into the hives of the new.
   Come, come; do not delay, new year bees—
Look what a wealth of parting gifts has been laid on the year as
                                   she leaves.

The fierce, destructive heat of Baiśākh will quickly seize

The *dolan-cãpã* buds that tremble now in the Caitra breeze.

  Finish all that they have to give, let nothing stay;
As the season ends let everything go in an orgy of giving away.
  Come, thieves of hidden honey; come now, bees—
The year has chosen to marry death and wants to give all as she
                                                              leaves.

Arrival of the Monsoon

Taufiq Rafat

This poem, written in English, celebrates the arrival of the monsoon whose life-giving rains mark the end of the oppressive heat of summer.

Before the thrust of this liberating wind
whatever is not fixed, has a place to go,
strains northwards to the coniferous lands.

And drunk with motion, clothes on the washing-line
are raised above themselves; a flapping sheet
turns a roof corner into a battlement.

Gliding days are over. The birds are tossed
sideways and back, and lifted against their will.
They must struggle to achieve direction.

A welcome darkness descends. Harsh contours
dissolve, lose their prosaic condition.
All the sounds we have loved are restored.

And now the rain! In sudden squalls
it sweeps the street, and equally sudden
are the naked boys paddling in the ditches.

Alive, alive, everything is alive again.
Savour the rain's coolness on lips and eyes.
How madly the electric wire is swinging.

From brown waters eddying round their hooves
the drenched trees rise and shake themselves,
and summer ends in a flurry of drops.

The Village Had No Walls

Vyankatesh Madgulkar
Translated by Ram Deshmukh

The novel *Village Without Walls*, from which this extract is taken was written in Marathi and tells the first-person story of a young schoolmaster assigned to a remote village. In the course of building up the village school he finds himself drawn into the lives of the villagers on many levels, and is entrusted with different tasks and responsibilities. Many of the villagers are shepherds; others, like Sheku in this passage, are farmers. Ayubu is a young man who has attached himself to the schoolmaster.

One day, while the sowing operation was at its height, Sheku came to see me. He was not often seen in the village. He had two or three acres of land outside the village and its cultivation was his only interest in life. It was early morning and the man had covered himself with a *dhoti*—as if it were a blanket. All I could see of him was his scraggy face and dusty feet—they looked leathery from constant trekking; the toes had coarse ungainly nails on them. His hands were hidden from view. Ayubu and I were by ourselves when Sheku came.

'Teacher,' he said, without bothering to sit down, 'do find me a bullock from somewhere. It's sowing time, you know!'

It was pointless to say that as schoolmaster I was not likely to own a bullock. He said, 'You can easily borrow one for me. I have one. The other died. I can sow if I get another. Otherwise it means starving—the whole year through.'

'Let me know first—Who has a bullock to lend? Then I can ask him.'

'Those that own bullocks have their own sowing to do. Who would put up with a delay in his own sowing? I have tried everywhere.'

'Whom do you want me to ask in that case?'

'Do what you like but help me in my need. The whole village says: "The schoolmaster is always helpful, always there in times of difficulty!" Why do you treat me differently?'

Ayubu, who had listened to all this without a word, now intervened. He turned his face towards Sheku and said:

'Are you crazy, Sheku? Where would the teacher get a bullock? Is he a farmer? Is he a cattle dealer? Have you no sense that you come and beg for whatever stupid thing enters your head? Go away!'

Sheku was obviously shaken—perhaps it was wrong of him to have asked.

'I—I am on my way, to be sure. But do try and do something for me if possible!' he said in a wheedling tone.

Ayubu got to his feet resolutely. Seizing the man by his elbows he propelled him down the steps and on to the road. He said:

'You are a fool, Sheku! As if the schoolmaster carries bullocks under his arms—in his clothes!'

Utterly crestfallen, Sheku went his way muttering something under his breath. Ayubu returned to his seat and said:

'You just ignore what he said, teacher! He is a simpleton . . .'

But I was unable to brush aside the feeling that it did not take the village people very far to teach them to read and write. Their needs were of a different sort altogether. Ayubu was without a family. Ananda needed bread, Sheku a bullock.

Two days later Sheku was still without his bullock although he had wandered far and wide, tried everywhere. He went home and slumped exhausted to the floor.

'It was useless,' he told his wife. Sheku's wife was a strapping woman, standing head and shoulders above all other women and half the men in the village. In the fields she did a man's work.

'Whom did you ask?' she inquired of her husband. He was sitting there—motionless, face buried in his hands, utterly dejected.

'All over the village, no one is prepared to give me a bullock.'

'What is to be done now?'

'We shall starve to death, that's all—kick up our heels and starve!'

The woman listened to her husband, saw the look in his eye, like that of a lamp which has nearly run out of oil.

'We start sowing tomorrow!' she said bravely.

'What about the bullock?'

'I shall get one.'

'Where from?'

'From wherever I please . . .'

'But . . .'

'What business is it of yours? I shall get the bullock. Just you go across to the field tomorrow morning. That's all.'

Sheku racked his brain; where was his wife going to find the bullock? In the morning he hoisted the plough on his shoulder and set off in the direction of his field leading his solitary bullock with his free hand. Once there, he turned his face towards the village and sat down on the embankment to await the arrival of his wife.

After an hour or so he saw her—she was alone. Sheku's face fell: 'The woman took a wager, but she was not able to find a bullock. There will be no sowing now. A bullock might become available after others have done their sowing. What good will that do? The crop will be backward in any case, not as usual, and if the crop does not yield enough grain for a full year we must starve; or roam from place to place in search of work . . .' Sheku had made himself utterly miserable by this brooding when his strapping spouse reached his side.

'Couldn't you get the bullock?'

'Why not? Get the plough ready.'

'But—where is the other bullock?'

'It is all right. Yoke the bullock at one end—I shall push at the other!'

Sheku shuddered at the thought. He found his voice with great difficulty, 'No, no, that can't be!' But the woman had made up her mind and she knew that she was strong enough for the job.

'This is no time for "whys" and "hows"—yoke the bullock.'

Seeing that her husband was incapable of movement, too dejected even to lift his head, she rose and herself put the bullock to the plough. Placing one end of the yoke across her own shoulder, she commanded: 'Now, rope me tight.'

At that the frail man hardened his heart, got up and signalled the bullock to move. The animal moved, so did the woman. The ploughshare pierced the earth, began furrowing a path through the damp soil. Sheku released a handful of millet seed into the hopper—the grain coursed down the bamboo tube, then leaped to the ground. Sheku's wife continued to pull by the side of the bullock through sheer determination.

The sowing went on all morning. At midday Sheku and his wife, breathless from the exertion, sat down to a quiet lunch. Sheku was tongue-tied; the woman spoke of this and that. Together they went to work with a rake until the seed was evenly covered by the upturned soil.

By evening they had sown the two-acre plot; then the exhausted trio made tracks for home.

Next day the incredible tale was all over the village. There was admiration, some astonishment—occasionally even a feeling of scornful amusement.

That night, on my way back from the school, I stood in front of Sheku's house for a moment. Inside, the lamp-light revealed the prostrate form of Sheku's wife by the side of a wall. Sheku stood on her back kneading her body with his feet. Supporting himself by placing both his hands on the wall he was massaging his wife's aching back with a slow movement of each foot.

I Left You Behind

Dawood Haider
Translated by Farida Majid

This poem, translated from the Bengali, powerfully evokes the plight of
a young couple when the man is forced to migrate from his poverty-
stricken village in search of work.

> I left you, my love,
>   I left you behind.
> Along with a worn out mat,
>   an oil-aged pillow,
> two cracked pans, a basket,
>   and a rusty shovel
> I left you behind
>   in a rotting hovel
> at the swampy edge
>   of the village.
>
> I left you, my love,
>   I left you behind.
> As you served my last meal
>   of wild yam-greens
> your sad face looked
>   into my averted eyes.
> Waving my hand
>   to chase off flies
> I watched the hungry
>   dog in the yard,
> I watched the circling
>   crow in the sun,
> and I watched your
>   sari stained with

silent tears when
          I left you behind.

I remember what I meant
          to say to you.
I wanted to leave
          you a few coins.
I wanted to tell
          the Munshi House people
to give you a job.
          I wanted to leave you
my scarf which you
          could wear besides
your only tattered sari.
          But I did not say
or do any of those things,
          I just left you behind.

The village is burnt out
          in the mid-April sun,
and I know it will be
          washed away in
the monsoon flood.
          It would be foolish
then to look from
          door to door for a job
or even a meagre meal.
          So I am now
on my way to town
          hoping to make
some kind of living.
          I had to leave
the village behind
          hoping to go on living.
I left you, my love,
          I left you behind.

Big Brother

Shekhar Joshi
Translated by Gordon C. Roadarmel

This short story, translated from the Hindi, describes how two people from the same village in the hills come to work in the big city (it could well be New Delhi), where they meet, are brought together by their common birthplace, and then driven apart.

Jagdish Babu saw him for the first time at the small café with the large signboard, on the left coming out of the marketplace. A fair complexion, sparkling eyes, golden-brown hair, and an unusual smooth liveliness in his movements—like a drop of water sliding along the leaf of a lotus. From the alertness in his eyes, one would guess his age at only nine or ten, and that's what it was.

When Jagdish Babu, puffing on a half-lit cigarette, entered the café, the boy was removing some plates from a table. But by the time Jagdish Babu had seated himself at a corner table, the boy was already standing in front of him, looking as though he'd been waiting for hours for him—for a person to sit in that seat. The boy said nothing. He did bow slightly, to show respect, and then just smiled. Receiving the order for a cup of tea, he smiled again, went off, and then returned with the tea in the twinkling of an eye.

Feelings are strange. Even isolated in a solitary and deserted place, a man may feel no loneliness. Despite the isolation, everything is very intimate, very much his own. In contrast, though, there is sometimes a feeling of loneliness even in a bustling setting among thousands of people. Everything there seems alien, lacking in intimacy. But that feeling of solitude and isolation inevitably has roots in a history of separation or detachment.

Jagdish Babu had come from a distant region and was alone. In the hustle and bustle of the marketplace, in the clamour of the café, everything seemed unrelated to himself. Maybe after living here for a while and growing accustomed to it, he'd start feeling some intimacy in the surroundings. But today the place seemed alien, beyond the boundary of belonging—far beyond. Then he began remembering nostalgically the people of his village region, the school and college boys there, the café in the nearby town.

'Tea, Sha'b!'

Jagdish Babu flicked the ash from his cigarette. In the boy's pronunciation of 'Sahab', he sensed something which he had been missing. He proceeded to follow up the speculation—'What's your name?'

'Madan.'

'Very well, Madan! Where are you from?'

'I'm from the hills, Babuji.'

'There are hundreds of hill places—Abu, Darjeeling, Mussoorie, Simla, Almora. Which hills is your village in?'

'Almora, Sha'b,' he said with a smile, 'Almora.'

'Which village in Almora?' he persisted.

The boy hesitated. Perhaps embarrassed by the strange name of the village, he answered evasively—'Oh it's far away, Sha'b. It must be fifteen or twenty miles from Almora.'

'But it still must have a name,' Jagdish Babu insisted.

'Dotyalgaon,' he responded shyly.

The strain of loneliness vanished from Jagdish Babu's face, and when he smiled and told Madan that he was from a neighbouring village, the boy almost dropped his tray with delight. He stood there speechless and dazed, as though trying to recall his past.

The past: a village . . . high mountains . . . a stream . . . mother . . . father . . . older sister . . . younger sister . . . big brother.

Whose shadow was it that Madan saw reflected in the form of Jagdish Babu? Mother?—No. Father?—No. Elder or younger sister?—No. Big brother?—Yes, Dajyu!

Within a few days, the gap of unfamiliarity between Madan

and Jagdish Babu had disappeared. As soon as the gentleman sat down, Madan would call out—'Greetings, Dajyu!' 'Dajyu, it's very cold today.' 'Dajyu, will it snow here too?' 'Dajyu, you didn't eat much yesterday.'

Then from some direction would come a cry—'Boy!' And Madan would be there even before the echo of the call could be heard. Leaving with the order, he would ask Jagdish Babu, 'Anything for you, Dajyu?'

'Bring me some water.'

'Right away, Dajyu,' Madan would call out from the other end of the room, repeating the word 'Dajyu' with the eagerness and affection of a mother embracing her son after a long separation.

After some time, Jagdish Babu's loneliness disappeared. Now not only the marketplace and the café but the city itself seemed painted with a sense of belonging. Madan's constant cry of 'Dajyu' ringing out from all over the room, however, no longer pleased him.

'Madan! Come here.'

'Coming, Dajyu!'

This repetition of the word 'Dajyu' aroused the bourgeois temperament in Jagdish Babu. The thin thread of intimacy could not survive the strong pull of ego.

'Shall I bring tea, Dajyu?'

'No tea. But what's this, "Dajyu, Dajyu" you keep shouting all the time? Have you no respect for a person's prestige?'

Jagdish Babu, flushed with anger, had no control over his words. Nor did he stop to wonder whether Madan could know the meaning of 'prestige'. But Madan, even with no explanation, had understood everything. Could one who had braved an understanding of the world at such a tender age fail to comprehend one paltry word?

Having made the excuse of a headache to the manager, Madan sat in his small room, head between his knees, and sobbed. In these circumstances far from home, his display of intimacy toward Jagdish Babu had been perfectly natural. But now, for the first time in a foreign place, he felt as though someone had pulled him from the lap of his mother, from the arms of his father, and from the protection of his sister.

Madan returned to his work as before.

The next day, heading for the café, Jagdish Babu suddenly met a childhood friend, Hemant. Reaching the café, Jagdish Babu beckoned to Madan, but he sensed that the boy was trying to remain at a distance. On the second call, Madan finally came over.

Today that smile was not on his face, nor did he say, 'What can I bring, Dajyu?' Jagdish Babu himself had to speak up— 'Two teas, two omelettes.'

Even then, instead of replying, 'Right away, Dajyu,' he said, 'Right away, Sha'b,' and then left, as though the man were a stranger.

'Perhaps a hill boy?' Hemant speculated.

'Yes,' muttered Jagdish Babu and changed the subject.

Madan had brought the tea.

'What's your name?' Hemant asked, as though trying to be friendly.

For a few moments silence engulfed the table. Jagdish Babu's lowered eyes were centred on the cup of tea. Memories swam before Madan's eyes—Jagdish Babu asking his name like this one day . . . then, 'Dajyu, you didn't eat much yesterday' . . . and one day, 'You pay no attention to anyone's prestige . . .'

Jagdish Babu raised his eyes and saw that Madan seemed about to erupt like a volcano.

'What's your name?' Hemant repeated insistently.

'Sha'b, they call me "Boy,"' he said quickly and walked away.

'A real blockhead,' Hemant remarked, taking a sip of tea. 'He can't even remember his own name.'

An Introduction

Kamala Das

Kamala Das writes poetry in English; she writes novels and short
stories in Malayalam. It is her decision to write in English that provides
the starting-point of this poem.

I don't know politics but I know the names
Of those in power, and can repeat them like
Days of week, or names of months, beginning with
Nehru. I am Indian, very brown, born in
Malabar. I speak three languages, write in
Two, dream in one. Don't write in English, they said,
English is not your mother-tongue. Why not leave
Me alone, critics, friends, visiting cousins,
Every one of you? Why not let me speak in
Any language I like? The language I speak
Becomes mine, its distortions, its queernesses
All mine, mine alone. It is half English, half
Indian, funny perhaps, but it is honest,
It is as human as I am human, don't
You see? It voices my joys, my longings, my
Hopes, and it is useful to me as cawing
Is to crows or roaring to the lions, it
Is human speech, the speech of the mind that is
Here and not there, a mind that sees and hears and
Is aware. Not the deaf, blind speech
Of trees in storm or of monsoon clouds or of rain or the
Incoherent mutterings of the blazing
Funeral pyre. I was child, and later they
Told me I grew, for I became tall, my limbs
Swelled and one or two places sprouted hair. When

I asked for love, not knowing what else to ask
For, he drew a youth of sixteen into the
Bedroom and closed the door. He did not beat me
But my sad woman-body felt so beaten.
The weight of my breasts and womb crushed me. I shrank
Pitifully. Then . . . I wore a shirt and my
Brother's trousers, cut my hair short and ignored
My womanliness. Dress in sarees, be girl,
Be wife, they said. Be embroiderer, be cook,
Be a quarreller with servants. Fit in. Oh,
Belong, cried the categorizers. Don't sit
On walls or peep in through our lace-draped windows.

Be Amy, or be Kamala. Or, better
Still, be Madhavikutty. It is time to
Choose a name, a role. Don't play pretending games.
Don't play at schizophrenia or be a
Nympho. Don't cry embarrassingly loud when
Jilted in love . . . I met a man, loved him. Call
Him not by any name, he is every man
Who wants a woman, just as I am every
Woman who seeks love. In him . . . the hungry haste
Of rivers, in me . . . the ocean's tireless
Waiting. Who are you, I ask each and everyone,
The answer is, it is I. Anywhere and
Everywhere, I see the one who calls himself
I; in this world, he is tightly packed like the
Sword in its sheath. It is I who drink lonely
Drinks at twelve, midnight, in hotels of strange towns,
It is I who laugh, it is I who make love
And then feel shame, it is I who lie dying
With a rattle in my throat. I am sinner,
I am saint. I am the beloved and the
Betrayed. I have no joys which are not yours, no
Aches which are not yours. I too call myself I.

Muniyakka

Lakshmi Kannan
Translated by the author

This contemporary short story, translated from Tamil, is set in Bangalore, a town in central southern India. The *sraddha* referred to is a ritual performed to mark the anniversary of someone's death.

Muniyakka had mastered the art of soliloquy. She would keep muttering to herself as she walked, mutter fluently, without any hesitation. Her most meaningful conversations were the ones she had with herself, and everyone was used to the way the old woman freely held forth.

Carrying herself on thin, spindly legs that looked like a pair of drumsticks, Muniyakka was surprisingly mobile as she went about her work, shivering in the cold winter of Bangalore. Sweeping, swabbing, washing vessels, washing clothes, cleaning the courtyards in front of houses, sweeping the yards and decorating them with skilfully patterned rangolis. As she went about her work, she would continuously and tirelessly talk to herself, 'argue' with her relations and enemies, and give herself suitable replies from them. Children playing on the sides of the street would laugh at her and cry out: 'There goes Muniyakka, the walkie-talkie!' Adults who chanced upon her, noticed her in passing, mildly amused. Muniyakka went about nonchalant, perpetuating a habit that seemed to sustain her even as she worked.

Washing vessels in Anjaneyulu's house brought her twenty rupees. She received another thirty-five for sweeping, swabbing the floors, and washing the clothes at Vasudev Chetty's. Having worked for a long period at the Rama Raos', she now received a kind of gratuity from them and they had allowed her to build a small hut for herself in a corner of their garden. She found it quite convenient. There was a tap near the hut and a raised stone platform over a cemented surface on which she washed her own clothes as well as those of the Rao household. She put her rags out to dry on a short washing line tied to a neem and a coconut tree on either side.

After finishing her work, Muniyakka would return to the Rao bungalow. Mrs Ratna Rao had a genial temperament and she treated Muniyakka like an old member of the family. No festivities took place in the house without her participation. Ratna Rao shared some of her free moments with the old woman, chatting about various things in a semi-serious vein. Only Ratna could truly relate to Muniyakka's strange ways and she found the old woman's queer humour truly enjoyable. Every day, Muniyakka concluded her day's work with her duties in the temple close by. This gave her fifteen rupees, apart from a sense of fulfilment. At the end of the day she cleaned and washed the floor of the temple, after which she gratefully took refuge in her hut in the Rao garden. She then heaved a sigh of relief and called it a day. Lighting an earthen oil lamp and guided by its dim glow, she got a log-fire crackling in a rather functional oven, and a pot to boil her broth in. After preparing the broth, she cooked some millet flour, cooked it really soft and tender, and made some curry to go with it. Then she sat down to eat.

Alone in the hut she ate, helping herself to large handfuls of the food. Scooping up the food with her palm, she swallowed morsel after morsel, freely scolding her dead husband and her absent sons. Eventually, losing the feeling that she was alone in the hut, her appetite whetted by her own anger, she ate her food ravenously. She was pleasantly suffused with the satisfaction of eating food earned through her own hard labour.

After finishing her meal, she cleaned up the hut meticulously, and with a piece of jaggery in hand, emerged to sit outside for some time. She nibbled on the jaggery lingeringly. After swallowing the last little morsel she sat back and chewed some areca-nut lazily, her eyes fixed on some distant point in the darkness. In that still moment, she felt quite empty. Her mind was swept clean like the interior of the hut, purged of all disturbing thoughts and stilled to a mute point. Not a fibre of her being moved. And yet, this sense of peace never lasted long . . .

With the failing vision of her old eyes, she peered into the inky darkness around her. The Rao bungalow was surrounded by a large garden. Segregated on one side was a clump of coconut trees. Beyond the coconut grove was a large, sprawling jack-fruit tree and nestling under the shade of this, Muniyakka's hut. Gardens and groves in Bangalore invariably howled with a strong breeze in the night. To Muniyakka's eyes, in the darkness of the night, the coconut trees seemed to sway with their 'hair' loosely flying in the breeze, dancing the dance of the devil. Kokkina Halli was Muniyakka's village, a few miles away from Bangalore. The people of that village always described ghosts and devils this way, essentially in their female forms: the devil, personified as a wild, mad woman, the incisors in her row of teeth curving outside on her lips to reveal a hideous smile, as her voice cackled and echoed resoundingly in the cloud-capped night sky. Hair swaying in the breeze and over the face as the devil danced in a trance to a mad rhythm.

Outside the house and above the wall that enclosed the garden, there was a big peepul tree under the dim glow of the moon. The oily gloss of its leaves shimmered in the night light. It was a garden pampered by the care and attention of the Rao couple. It had a rich variety of plants and many flower and fruit bearing trees. Lush and healthy, bursting with flowers, fruits and vegetables, it exuded a sense of luxuriant well-being, character-istic of any well-maintained garden in Bangalore. Looking at it, one could forget for a moment that there were things like abject poverty or squalor or disease, elsewhere. Collectively, the trees and plants looked like children who had been brought up with care and affection. Muniyakka was very fond of the garden and lavished her affection on it. In the afternoons, she would compete with the gardener and pour bucket after bucket of water, covering the entire garden, even if the exercise threatened to break her back. For a few moments, the flowers and fruits would take on a golden hue under the Midas touch of the setting sun. Taking in the sight, Muniyakka would feel infinitely enriched, as if she had somehow inherited great wealth. And yet, when the sky darkened . . .

She was back in her retreat again, squatting outside her hut in the darkness to look at the same swaying plants and trees in the menacing form of the devil's dance. Her heart quickened as it learned to keep pace with the devil's rhythm outside. In the turbulence of the breeze, the branches hissed like so many sinister snakes and, in the fury of the hissing, Muniyakka could completely identify herself. Her mind danced, pulsating with the rhythm of the *dhvamsha* of Kali.

Sounds of windows being slammed and bolted. The servants of the Rao household and his oldest daughter were securing the windows against the cold and wild breeze outside. Through the glass windows, the light of the house spread a quiet glow in the middle of the dark garden. There was peace inside. But outside, a night pitch dark. Each leaf on the trees, fanning out like the enlarged hood of a snake, sighing 'shoo' 'shoo' 'shoo' as they together surrounded the solitary Muniyakka like a thousand hissing snakes.

Snakes and snakes and more snakes . . . everywhere a snake, hissing. If it slithers in green or brown colours in front of you, or if you find it curling down from the eaves of the ceiling, then take a sturdy bamboo pole and bring it down hard on the snake, beat it up instantly! Beat on it till it quivers in agony and is smashed into pulp. But if the same genus of serpent comes crowned with the title of Cobra and you see the proud tilt of its hood and feel the heat of its hissing breath, then reach for some milk immediately. Offer the milk most humbly to the cobra, kneel down and do your obeisance. If the same cobra does not slide or slither but is frozen in stone in the corner of a temple, or under a blackberry tree, then there is no limit to your worship. You apply kumkum on the stone snake, dash your own forehead on the curved stone as you entreat favours and dreams that need to be fulfilled. Offer flowers to the stone snake, break coconuts and let the tender coconut water bathe the stone as you repeat your prayers, shivering and damp from your holy ablutions, your

41

stomach caved in from a devout fast. These women, muttering their prayers, going round and round the stone snakes and the blackberry tree, round and round dizzily like fervent dervishes. Ripe berries dropping from the tree on the stone snakes below, smashing their rich pulp against the stone and dying it in vivid spots of blue and purple. The dumb mouths of the snakes carrying the sweets smeared by the women. Armies of large, black ants filing in orderly rows toward the sweets. Stones scarred with lines of kumkum, turmeric, sandalwood paste, and the smudgy sprinkling of withered petals of flowers.

It was Muniyakka's responsibility to wash the stones clean of all the stains. She doused them with buckets of water, and with a rough coir brush in her hand, fiercely scrubbed the stains away. With a broomstick held firmly in her hand, she swept away the stones of the half-eaten berries dropped by the squirrels. She cursed the women who came to worship and made such a mess at the temple. 'Foolish women . . . banging their brows on the stone, begging for favours—Give me a son, Lord of Snakes, Great Nagaraja! Please give me a son . . . Idiots! I was like you when I was a young woman, bruising my brow on this stone and praying for sons. The result? Today I have three useless sons in whom I had a deep, implicit faith. I visited their homes so eagerly, but not one of them would even give me a single tepid bowl of broth. Each worthless son, lusting after his own wife. They don't need a mother any more. Shameless bastards. Naturally! They were, after all, fathered by an equally worthless man, Bairappa. That husband of mine, dying after leading a life of waste—smoking, drinking, gambling, squandering my hard-earned money . . . Bairappa be damned!'

'So, what news, *ajji*? Finished your work for the day?' asked Thimmayya, the temple gardener, emerging from the bushes.

'Yes, Thimmayya, I've finished my work. But I will have to get up early tomorrow. It is the death anniversary of that worthless husband of mine, Bairappa. I will do my duty and have a small *sraddha* in my hut. Come tomorrow and have a special lunch. Will you come?'

'Of course, *ajji*, I'll certainly come,' said Thimmayya with a big grin. Then he asked, '*Ajji*, have you bought all the things necessary for the *sraddha* or has anything been left out? You always take care not to leave any gaps in Bairappa's banana leaf—complete with his favourite brand of *bidi*, sweet buns made with jaggery, then spiced rice . . . even the toddy. Mmm . . .' Thimmayya licked his lips in candid anticipation of an appetising meal.

Muniyakka laughed out loud. 'Alright then, come tomorrow. You can have everything from the bastard Bairappa's leaf.' Picking up her bucket and the broomstick, she went out of the temple.

Bairappa's *sraddha*. It was done just the way it had been all these years. Muniyakka performed the rites that should rightfully have been performed by her sons. But they ignored the day. She kept all her husband's favourite dishes on a clean banana leaf, meant to appease his departed soul. The gleaming leaf held fish curry, tenderly cooked cabbage, sweet buns made with jaggery, spiced rice, a small bottle of toddy and a packet of his favourite brand of *bidis*. On this day, Muniyakka had a youthful glow on her face. Today she felt emboldened to wear a large, round kumkum on her forehead. Flowers in her hair. A clean cotton sari wrapped around her old, withered body. She briskly attended to all the rites and rituals of the *sraddha*, all the while scolding and cursing her husband. Ratna Rao saw the items on the banana leaf and had a good laugh. She teased Muniyakka pleasantly, her voice ringing lightly like silver bells. Muniyakka blushed at the teasing but joined Mrs Rao in her light-hearted laughter. When she got through all the work, Muniyakka began to sweep and clean the hut and her face registered a subtle transformation: 'Husband! Son! What a humbug these relationships are . . . Hum!' She came out of the hut as usual and squatted outside, back resting against the wall, eyes peering into the darkness. The tree began to dance. Muniyakka enjoyed the devil's dance once more, with a vicarious pleasure. In that lonely hour she experienced her own sense of isolation with a private thrill. Felt the damp air caressing her hollow cheeks, the pleasant smell of the earth dampened by the prelude of a drizzle.

Muniyakka smelt everything around her and heard the distant thunder. I won't have to water the garden tomorrow, she thought. There will be a heavy downpour. Thunder will crack the sky and rain will pour down on all the trees. And the plants. And on this hut, here. The temple. The stone snakes. Everything will be washed clean.

In the strong breeze, the branches swayed wildly. Muniyakka waited for the trees to begin the dance of the devil. Waited quietly, to participate in the dance. She sat in the darkness, a small speck, peering, watching, thinking:

> Who's a devil? And who's not a devil?
> Who am I?
> And you? Who the devil are you?
> Where am I going? And when? For what?
> And up to where?

Across the Black Waters

Mulk Raj Anand

Across the Black Waters, first published in 1940, is an English-language novel which takes as its subject-matter the Indian soldiers, or sepoys, who fought on the Allied side in France in the First World War. Lalu, the central character, is a young Sikh from a village in the Punjab, and the first of these two extracts describes an attack and subsequent retreat. In the second passage Lalu has been assigned to work as an orderly in the regimental headquarters (the 'Babus' are the clerks who regularly work there). The conversation between Lalu and Adjutant Owen refers to the attack described in the first passage.

1

The attack was to commence about three o'clock.

The sepoys were ready a little earlier. Some stood by their rifles, others sat on their haunches. Their packs were beside them. They didn't know what to do with their time. There were not even the proverbial flies to kill. And their heads hung down with the weight of slow, heavy moments. Now and then terrific detonations of guns enveloped the air. It seemed as if the attack had begun and they stretched their hands towards their packs ready to go. But there was no sign of Havildar Lachman Singh. And they waited again in suspense, relieved only by the uncanny sight of Daddy Dhanoo dozing where he had sat mumbling the name of God to the rosary of his heart.

'Woe to the enemy if they see such warriors as Dhanoo,' said Lalu.

'He came to this world to worship, but he has been set to ginning,' said Uncle Kirpu, likening the noise of gun fire to that in a primitive cotton factory.

'Oon, hain, what . . .' Daddy Dhanoo said, opening his heavy-lidded eyes and smiling apologetically.

'Nothing, nothing, there is no talk,' Kirpu assured him. 'You go to sleep; only don't snore or you will frighten the enemy.'

Daddy Dhanoo needed no encouragement, however. The food he had eaten at midday, the snuff he had snuffed and his general sense of fatality drugged him into a stupor which made him impervious to everything except orders. Though he had hoped on the outbreak of the war that he would be disqualified from service abroad and sent on pension, he had had no objections to the idea of going to fight and die in foreign lands. 'It is the orders of the Sarkar,' he had said. And when Uncle Kirpu had waxed ironically eloquent about 'Duty', Daddy Dhanoo had just sat stupefied and uncomprehending in his innocence, asking Lalu, 'Tell me, son, you are learned, what is the war all about?' For to him, 'Obedience' and 'Duty' were with 'God' not only the ultimate laws of the Universe, but inter-changeable. If loyalty to the spirit which creates the Universe was only possible through worship and the remembrance of the Almighty, then the 'obedience' to the Sarkar, whose salt one had eaten, was the highest 'Dharma'. And his pantheism was activist; it demanded the utmost sacrifice of which he was capable. He heard badly, but his ears seemed surprisingly sensitive to the words of officers; his eyes were bleary and weak and often remained closed in sleep, but they opened, red-streaked and big, and nearly popped out of their sockets, if he saw a superior coming; his rough, shapeless body was awkward in the ordinary way but he could keep his step in a route march when everyone else flagged; his head which could only grasp the elemental life was capable of infinite shades of subtlety if it came to the interpretation of what was right and what was wrong according to the unwritten code of military law summed-up in 'Duty'; and everything else was reduced to the test of the heart, the ultimate arbiter. This all-pervading sense of 'Dharma' spread like an invisible cancer through his system, the cancer which had eaten through him, till there was not much vitality left in the resources of his hardy hillman's will and he had to nourish his resignation on snuff and more snuff.

The gunfire died down for a moment.

There was still no sign of Lachman, but Jemadar Subah Singh and Lance-Naik Lok Nath came with hasty flourishes of their arms.

'Be in readiness and alert! Get your packs,' said Jemadar Subah Singh in emphatic whispers, assuming a surreptitious manner as if he were preparing to play a game.

'Has Lachman told you what to do?' Lok Nath asked, affecting a stern cordiality as he lengthened the shadow of his presence over the men.

And before they had answered, he began to explain to them: 'Between this trench and the enemy there is a space of level ground which ends in a jungle on the right flank. The Gora regiments on our right may be pressed hard and may be forced to fall back. So we . . .'

'We know that but what are we waiting for?' asked Kharku.

'When you get up there,' continued Lok Nath ignoring the interruption, 'you must remember to take advantage of the unexpectedness of our attack. The Germans will be ignorant of our arrival and the sahibs say that they fear us. They think we are all Gurkhas with kukhries in our mouths, savages who will creep up to them, take them by surprise and kill them. And the Sarkar is treating you as the shock troops for that reason. Now you show them some of your savagery. All brave men like hand-to-hand fighting. And I have always tried to instil in you the fact that as brave sepoys, you must charge the enemy without fear with your bayonets, wherever you find him, and hit him in a vital spot. Aim at the heart, remember, the belly or the testicles of the enemy! If he has the advantage in attack, swiftly fell him with a blow from the butt end of your rifle and trample upon him and drive the bayonet deep into the body, and draw it out so that he bleeds and dies . . . Understand? . . . acha?' And he warmed a curious red as he finished his lecture.

'We must go and give the final instructions to the other platoons,' said Jemadar Subah Singh.

'Come of your own accord, go with your own desire,' said Kirpu confronting them both bluntly.

But neither of the two toughs was in the mood to notice

Kirpu's banter or rudeness, so puffed-up were they in the glory and might of the role assigned to them to save the day for the Sarkar by dint of their 'savagery'.

After Lok Nath's enumeration of the tender spots as the heart, the belly, and the testicles, the curiosity which had turned to fear in Lalu became the horror of several bayonet points sticking into his own belly. It was strange that they were aimed at no other point but the belly, as if there was no other vulnerable part of his body. But he could see his entrails with the dark liver hanging to them like the inside of the diseased oxen which the village cobbler butchered by the swamps in Nandpur. He would have to kill if he didn't get killed first, the thought suddenly came to him. Anyhow whether he killed or did not kill he would have to go there where the enemy was.

Involuntarily he trembled. Then he tried to remember the tactics of bayonet fighting, like a schoolboy recalling his lesson just before entering the examination room. And, like the frightened schoolboy, he felt he had forgotten, and the dread loomed before his eyes, occupying the hollow of his body which shook against his will.

He tried to steady himself so that he could become neutral, like his companions, who sat patient and tranquil though rather pale and silent, as if they were reflecting on their doom and yet seeking to control their flesh from giving any sign of weakness, each to his own, as if everyone were alone in this ordeal.

The artillery barrage was increasing. Lachman Singh came rushing like an angry bull, slipping in the sluggish mud, falling, tottering and furious. With his hand on his heart he stopped for the barest second to take breath. Then he said: 'The Connaughts are ahead of us. Get your packs. Up we go. Keep them in sight.' And then, as if he had regained the lightness of the old gymnast he was, he leapt up to the parapet.

Spurred on by Lachman, the whole platoon was climbing. Lalu took the parapet in a jump, dragging his rifle butt first, unafraid now, but feeling as if by handling the musket upside down he had begun badly.

The suddenness with which Lachman Singh uprooted them made them slightly unsteady. And they were surprised after days of bending in the trenches, to find themselves stretched almost to their full heights, rushing along towards the enemy. Some of the Connaughts on their right had already advanced about a hundred to a hundred and fifty yards, and the Baluchis of the 129th were out on the left.

The gun fire seemed to rend the air with a deafening roar. The clusters of mist which hung down from the sky were melting in a slow drizzle. The ground was difficult with stakes, roots and deep declivities, rising unevenly like low hills and then sloping suddenly to fall away beyond the end of the Connaughts' line.

Lalu ran with his head bent forward, as if by so doing he expected to avert any bullets that might come his way. The particles of rain seemed to freeze on his flesh. He shivered a little and ran with a gurgling noise in his throat.

A hail of bullets scattered the men and Lachman Singh shouted to them to lie down and crawl.

A thick ragged blanket of darkness seemed to cover them as they inclined to the earth. The smoke of the guns had mixed with the curtain of rain.

As he dragged himself forward he could only see the rumps, the packs, the swinging hands and heavy feet of the men.

Some of the Connaught Goras seemed to have run about five hundred yards ahead. Kirpu and Dhanoo were several yards behind him, following like ghostly shadows with their eyelashes, eyebrows, their turbans and the serge of their coats whitened by the mist, while Lachman, Kharku, and Hanumant were ahead of him. The foreknowledge of death swished past him with the tempestuous music of the bullets. And now the mist reeked of a sulphurous powder as it clung clammy and wet like venom on the skin.

Lachman Singh turned and shouted; 'Get abreast of the Connaughts.'

Taken aback by the order, they hesitated, then hurtled forward, falling over each other.

Lalu got abreast of Kharku and shaded his eyes to look for the Tommies. They seemed invisible, except perhaps as the gestures of falling men in the distance.

He stopped to take breath, for a withering rifle fire rent the air. There was a swamp with the stubble of a bush half buried in it, at his feet. He jumped across it panting. The detonations seemed to throw up great clods of earth and limbs and smoke along the line. He did not know what to do, where to go, whether to advance or retreat, for Lachman Singh had swerved towards the left and run to the end of the company, while Kharku had doubled-up with a shell fragment and fallen.

He was convulsed by the volleys of machine-gun fire which came in the train of explosions on the left where the heavies seemed to be bursting.

He lay down and began to crawl. For a moment he was cut off from everyone. And he felt as he had felt once when as a child he had gone with his parents to a cattle fair and had got lost and had run in a panic, weeping salty tears, looking for someone he could recognize. Another crash and a whirlwind of earth and smoke flew up from an explosion near him, while rifle and machine-gun fire poured down like a rainstorm.

'Oh pity! Wah Guru!' he shrieked as the swish of steel and gusts of smoke and mounds of earth and iron blew past him.

'Turn back!' the voices of officers came.

To be sure no one could go forward in the face of that fire. But having come so far Lalu felt he would have gone farther. And strangely enough he had forgotten to be afraid.

He turned round, running in short capers with bent back, then lay flat, crawled on his hands and knees, stopped and ran again. He stumbled upon a pit and fell, deafened, his heart crying with a passionate anger.

'Oh the steel!' he mumbled even as he wondered how he would reach the trenches alive and who would be left behind dead, besides Kharku. A great many Tommies had fallen. Kirpu, Dhanoo—he wondered whether they were safe. And Lachman Singh?

He felt all over his stomach as he crawled in the shell hole where he found himself, to see if there was any blood on his body. Only the damp of rain and mud came up with his hand. He halted to breathe and coughed to ease his throat: a queer growling noise came out of his lungs, half sob, half moan, a broken, hoarse grief that receded into the silence of his larynx even as the detonations of the artillery barrage smothered everything ahead of him. Fear gripped his throat.

'Come on, son,' he heard Lachman Singh whispering to him. And he espied the form of NCO dragging Kharku's body in the mud.

'Which is dearest, work or your hide, asked the iron tongue?' Lalu heard Kirpu's voice behind him.

'And what did you answer?' the boy queried.

'The hide of course, the hide,' said Kirpu, sweating and breathless. And he came abreast of Lalu, stopped for a moment, and covered his face with his hands as if to prevent himself from coughing or moaning or sobbing and then went on.

The boy was moved by some instinctive weakness to creep up to him and shouted to him:

'I hope nothing has happened to you.'

'I am all right, son . . .' Kirpu began, but he was hoarse with fatigue and could not finish the answer.

'Where is Dhanoo?' Lalu asked, his loud voice crumbling among the bursting fragments of the shells.

Uncle Kirpu looked back and, not finding Dhanoo, waved his head to signify that he did not know.

The suspense was wearing him down.

But just then he saw part of the company on his left retreating.

'Come on, boys,' Lachman called.

Lalu craned his neck, lifted himself, and followed Lachman. In a moment he was helping to drag Kharku, who had lain by the Havildar. The dead face was twisted into an ugly grimace, his mouth stretched open apparently through the writhing of some deep pain he had suffered before he died. Lalu's legs were shaking involuntarily, but he helped Lachman to heave the dead body and they proceeded, their feet slipping in the mud, their torsos strained forward . . . They were almost running now, losing consciousness of the yards, losing touch with everyone . . .

The cyclone of bullets was still rushing overhead.

He ducked his back and sat on his knees for a moment as if he were a Muhammadan who had suddenly stopped to say prayers before the gates of hell. He swept the right flank with a glance as he struggled to lie down. Lachman also dropped Kharku's body and rested.

A sepoy doubled up with an agonized groan and another caught his head and, throwing his rifle away, set to wiping mud on a wound on his leg; while, farther away in a clearing, the sepoys were crawling back or lay huddled for safety.

The lead whined and whimpered while the shells crashed after a curious gurgle in the darkening sky as if God were enjoying himself mightily at this destruction.

And not an inch of the ground seemed immune from the metal, not even the parapet of their trenches, now only six or seven yards away. They had apparently advanced three hundred yards before meeting the hurricane of fire.

'Come, push along and don't bar the way,' Kirpu called.

Lalu dragged Kharku's flagging body till he got to the parapet. Then he let himself drop into the trench through sheer exhaustion, pulling the body after him.

When they got back it all seemed to have happened in a flash, the whole violent, furious, breathless rush towards the enemy, the protracted, unending shocks of fire and then the retreat.

'Bale! Oh, Bale! Bale!' Kirpu belched after he had poured a draught of water down his throat.

'Why did we have to attack if we had to retreat?' Lalu said in order to drown the shattering ache of confusion at the back of his head, as if a post-mortem would help.

'We were exposed from the front and the flanks, son,' said Lachman Singh. 'We were badly exposed. The enemy artillery built up a barrage against us. And we lost touch with the Connaughts . . .'

'It was that fog, the rape of its mother,' said Kirpu.

'Han, the mist was a nuisance,' admitted Lachman with a strained smile.

'Where were our guns?' Lalu ventured tentatively. 'I thought they would cover our advance.'

'I don't know what happened to our guns,' Lachman said palely.

'Where are our guns? Where are our guns?—We haven't got any guns!' burst Kirpu with a red hot anger. 'The big guns, the big guns, we haven't got any big guns, otherwise they could have saved the Goras on the right from destruction. The support of the big guns . . . I tell you, if we had had big guns and more big guns, we could have silenced the opposite tornado of shrapnel and bullets. But this bitch of a Sarkar hasn't got as many big guns as the Germans . . .'

'How do you know?' Lachman Singh asked, assuming a sternness which Lalu had never seen in him.

'One of the Tommies there told me,' said Kirpu as he flung himself down with a shake of his head and began to light a cigarette.

For a moment everything was still and the three of them crouched, lay, or leaned back. Havildar Lachman Singh's face was hard, drawn, and pitiless as if he were choking with resentment. He seemed to know that it was wrong for him and for the Sarkar not to tell the soldiers the truth. And yet the instinct of the disciplined soldier of the Sarkar, who had earned his position by dint of the qualities of courage and persistence, quarrelled with the kindliness he had always brought to the treatment of the men. He seemed to say to himself: 'What has all that about the guns got to do with the men? I myself don't know how strong the Sarkar is. From the talk of the sahibs we seem to have come in time to save a very bad situation. But what has that got to do with us? . . . I hate to have to order you to your death. But what can I do? This is our Destiny, since we took the oath of service to the Sarkar!'

Lalu looked at him from the aura of his own indifference and tiredness: there was a hurt tenderness in Lachman's embarrassed smile and tears in the Havildar's eyes.

He tried to break the mask of his own resignation, twitched with a curious agitation and sought to ask himself what the Havildar felt. But the apathy of his fatigue congealed his blood, and he could only say: 'Don't mind this clown, Holdara.'

At that instant a runner came shouting in the dark as if he were drunk, 'Holdar Lachman Singh!'

'Coming,' Lachman answered.

'The Karnel Sahib was hit in the shoulder and you are to report to the Ajitan Sahib,' the runner said, surveying Lalu and Kirpu as if with the eyes of another world.

'What happened, do you know?' Lachman asked him, referring to the attack.

'The Goras are said to have rushed the enemy trenches and captured an officer and two men,' the runner blustered. 'They lost touch with the 69th in the dark . . . But the sahibs think that the behaviour of our troops was good considering it was our first action, and they have asked the Indian officers to tell the men that the British officers appreciate the disappointment of the sepoys at being asked to retire before coming to grips with the enemy.'

Lachman nodded as if he were listening and yet not listening.

'There were eleven casualties in the regiment,' the runner said freshly. And then he asked: 'Any in this platoon?'

'Yes,' said Lachman. 'Sepoy Kharku was killed.'

'Ohe, and where is Dhanoo?' Kirpu suddenly asked Lalu.

Lalu sat up, looked around himself, and said: 'Where is he? He was behind you.'

Uncle Kirpu got up and scurried up to the parapet like a madman, surveying the ground.

'No, he is not up there,' said Lachman. 'I surveyed the ground thoroughly for the dead and wounded before I returned.'

'Come, Holdara,' the runner urged.

As the two men walked away, Kirpu beat his forehead with his right hand and fell back in a stupor of exhaustion, while Lalu explored the cold dark with his brooding, enigmatic face. The rain was still drizzling and the water trickled down the clouded ditches with a sinister noise.

That night Lalu was crazed by dark thoughts which crumbled like agitated phantoms in his head and swirled before his sleep-weighted eyes.

He lay knotted in the dugout twisting his shoulders into his armpits to ward off the chill that came creeping into his flesh through the mounds of damp earth. But the rain dripped outside and the rumbling echoes of fire abused his sleep.

He tried to assimilate his quaking limbs. The vague weight of sadness for the missing Dhanoo, however, lingered like a ghost in the vacuum.

Afraid but tired he sought to lull himself into a half sleep. As he lay thus in foetal sleep he remembered how he had snuggled in the barn where Thiba and Rondu and Suchi slept, in the severe winters at home, the winters during which his mother used to give him a sweet semolina plum with a tumbler of hot milk before he went to bed, the winters during which he used to eat hot maize bread cakes and the spinach of mustard . . . As the ration party had failed to come back this evening his mouth watered at the memory of these delicacies.

He drew the blanket on to his face and tried not to think. He hugged himself in the cold gloom of the deluge. The mournful refrain of a cowherd's song came to his throat and soon he was drifting on the track of another dream memory: He was a child and his mother was singing him to sleep on a cot in the courtyard at the end of the day, even though she was tired. She seemed to have an amazing, inexhaustible energy as she went from one job to another, tirelessly, day and night. On his last visit to Nandpur, he recalled that her hair seemed to have turned all grey and her face was wrinkled, yet she had not lost the shapeliness of her features. And there was a living vitality in her that filled the home which would seem like a graveyard after she was gone.

He felt that he was suffocating as he lay hooded in the blanket, and uncovered his face. There was the thud, thud of an ache behind his head and he wished he could drown it in sleep.

Applying the famous formula of counting sheep as they passed through the gate of a fold, he dozed. But behind the sheep came cows and goats and bulls and elephants hurtling in quick succession into his brain, till he felt stupid to have to resort to such tricks in order to make himself rest.

And lo, the roaming, restless images of the past receded into the vacuum, and he fell asleep.

2

While he was still pottering about with the duster and zealously cultivating what he imagined to be European skill and efficiency in the rearrangements of the objects d'art in the room, there was a shuffling of forms outside the hall and the orderly was presenting arms to someone who seemed from the easy, soft Hindustani of his 'Salaam' to be Owen Sahib.

With an impetuosity that burst the bounds of discipline, Lalu went to the door and saluted the Sahib.

'Ah, Lal Singh,' said the Adjutant with that smile with which he had greeted him when the boy had come as a recruit in charge of the recruiting havildar. 'So you have come through unscathed, eh?' And, with a familiarity that hadn't the slightest trace of discipline, but was more akin to tenderness, Owen Sahib pulled Lalu's cheek and laughed.

'And Huzoor—Huzoor's arm?' Lalu said, seeing the Sahib's left arm in a sling.

Babu Khushi Ram, Thanoo Singh, and Muhammad Din came into the hall and, trying to put as much efficiency as they could into their limbs used to soldiering on paper, saluted.

'Hallo, Khushi Ram, still alive? Thanoo Singh, no more flesh on your bones yet? . . . Muhammad Din, how many mistakes in figures?' Owen Sahib greeted each according to his deserts and, putting his hat on a stand, went towards the head clerk.

'Where is my office?'

'Here, Huzoor. The CO and you are together in this room,' said Khushi Ram, nervous and panicky, walking and running as he led their way. 'Ohe, Lal Singh, come and dust the Sahib's chair,' he called as an afterthought.

'All right, Khushi Ram, don't fuss,' said the Sahib. 'Where is Major Peacock?'

'Huzoor, gone to headquarters,' answered Khushi Ram, standing to attention while the Sahib stood by the fire and began to take a cigarette out of his case.

Khushi Ram was too obsequious to see the difficulties of the Sahib with the cigarette, because of his sling, and still stood rigid. But Lalu advanced, in spite of the stare of the head clerk, took the match box from the mantelpiece and gave Owen Sahib a light. Then he began to dust the furniture.

'Huzoor, are you quite recovered?' Babu Khushi Ram asked.

The Sahib flushed a little, waved his head and evaded the question by asking:

'Well, what do you think of the war, Khushi Ram?'

Perhaps, because the adjutant of a regiment combines the function of a kind of deputy CO with clerical work of all kinds, he invariably establishes a familiarity with the office staff, which leads to an abeyance of the military virtues deriving from the shooting range, the parade ground, and 'quarter guard' and makes for humanity. At the best of times, however, the position of the Babus is somewhat invidious, as they are spicy pickles of military and civilian behaviour. How the sahibs respond to this depends on the state of their palate. And the Babus, completely insensitive to military values, try to find out how jaded is there appetite at any particular time.

'War, sir,' the Babu said, standing on the fence as it were, 'war has its drawbacks! Men get killed. And women and children starve. But it has its advantages also. It seems to clear our minds, making us able to see straightforward. It makes things simpler even at the cost of bloodshed. We are able to do things in wartime which we seem unable to do in peace. War brings out the bravery of people like Huzoor.'

This was flattery with a vengeance. The Sahib wondered what Khushi Ram really felt behind these words.

'And what do you think of war, Lal Singh?' the Sahib said, flicking the ash of his cigarette and scraping his boots on the fender, perhaps in order to give a natural and unofficial air to his enquiry.

But, nevertheless, Lalu was startled by so direct a question from the Sahib and could hardly think of an answer or dare to give an opinion out of respect and fear. And yet for these very reasons he had to say something.

'Huzoor, Havildar Lachman Singh is dead,' he blurted out, since he knew of the special friendship which had always existed between Owen Sahib and Lachman, gymnastic instructor, saint, hockey player, and the most popular NCO in the regiment.

'Yes, I know,' said the Ajitan Sahib, and bent his head.

'Huzoor,' continued Lal Singh to cover the tension that seemed imminent. 'The air and the water of this place is different. And because we were separated and put with English and French regiments, most of the sepoys felt that no one knew anything about us, and, some of the sepoys not knowing the language, lost their way . . . and it was . . . like hell! . . .'

The Sahib sauntered slowly over to where he stood and patted the boy, hesitated, and patted him again, as if consoling him for some loss, and then said, 'Bravo!'

'There are heavy casualty lists, Huzoor,' said Khushi Ram, now swinging over to another line of approach as he perceived that this sahib was, unlike other sahibs, rather eccentric and not quite so enthusiastic about the war. 'And the shelling must have been very terrible because some shrapnel even fell here in this village . . . I hear the ground over which the battle raged was difficult . . .'

'There was little or no cover,' said the Sahib, 'and the ground was waterlogged . . .' He winced as he said this and then, after a puff at his cigarette, continued: 'Rain fell all the time and the trenches were deep in mud and water . . . Terrible!'

'It seemed a gunnery duel from here, sir,' ventured Khushi Ram.

'Rather one-sided,' said Owen Sahib, 'because we hadn't many guns . . .'

'Uncle Kirpu said so,' Lalu mumbled to repress himself when he found that the Sahib had confirmed his friend's prognostications about the absence of artillery to back the British lines.

'Who is that?' the Sahib asked.

'Kirpu, Huzoor. Sepoy Kirpu Ram,' answered Lal Singh.

'Lance-Naik Kirpu Ram,' Babu Khushi Ram corrected.

'Oh Uncle Kirpu, um, give him my salaams and congratulations!' said Owen Sahib with a smile. 'He fought well! All the sepoys fought well . . .'

'They may help to save the cause of civilization,' said Khushi Ram, pandering to what he imagined was every sahib's idea in this war.

'You mean, they may become victims of civilization,' said the adjutant, suppressing his annoyance. And then, excusing the Babu for a phrase to which the Sarkar had given currency, and which he knew Khushi Ram was only repeating to flatter him, he said, more impersonally: 'All the rules, the theorems, all the ideas—everything has been shattered in this war, buried in the mud . . .'

Babu Khushi Ram stood guilty and apologetic and silent, his head bent, and felt he had made the Sahib angry.

The tension communicated itself to Lalu, who wished he had never come into this office, for the Babu might take it out of him for being a witness to his discomfiture.

'Oh well, buck up, Khushi Ram,' said Captain Owen, coming over and patting the Babu with a deliberately happy air. 'Civilization also means a sense of humour, you know. Don't let us fall victims to the mere solemnity of civilization . . .'

'I am your servant, Huzoor,' said Khushi Ram, a little relieved.

'Come along, then, and help me to get some work done,' said the Sahib. 'Is Lal Singh orderly here?'

'Yes, Huzoor, and, as he is literate, he is going to write the sepoys' letters for them,' answered Khushi Ram respectfully. And, turning to the boy with the efficiency of a frightened superior, he said: 'Lal Singh, the Sahib is going to work.'

As Lalu withdrew he knew he had Owen Sahib's sympathy.

Jejuri

Arun Kolatkar

These poems come from a recently published sequence, *Jejuri*, written in English. Jejuri is a small town in Maharashtra, in western India, where the temples of Khandoba attract many pilgrims. Kolatkar's poems describe a visit made by the poet-narrator to the temples.

Heart of Ruin

The roof comes down on Maruti's head.
Nobody seems to mind.

Least of all Maruti himself.
May be he likes a temple better this way.

A mongrel bitch has found a place
for herself and her puppies

in the heart of the ruin.
May be she likes a temple better this way.

The bitch looks out at you guardedly
past a doorway cluttered with broken tiles.

The pariah puppies tumble over her.
May be they like a temple better this way.

The black eared puppy has gone a little too far.
A tile clicks under its foot.

It's enough to strike terror in the heart
of a dung beetle

and send him running for cover
to the safety of the broken collection box

that never did get a chance to get out
from under the crushing weight of the roof beam.

No more a place of worship this place
is nothing less than the house of god.

The Priest's Son

these five hills
are the five demons
that khandoba killed

says the priest's son
a young boy
who comes along as your guide
as the schools have vacations

do you really believe that story
you ask him

he doesn't reply
but merely looks uncomfortable
shrugs and looks away

and happens to notice
a quick wink of a movement
in a scanty patch of scruffy dry grass
burnt brown in the sun
and says

look
there's a butterfly
there

The Butterfly

There is no story behind it.
It is split like a second.
It hinges around itself.

It has no future.
It is pinned down to no past.
It's a pun on the present.

It's a little yellow butterfly.
It has taken these wretched hills
under its wings.

Just a pinch of yellow,
it opens before it closes
and closes before it o

where is it

Hills

hills
demons
sand blasted shoulders
bladed with shale

demons
hills
cactus thrust
up through ribs of rock

hills
demons
kneequartz
limestone loins

demons
hills
cactus fang
in sky meat

hills
demons
vertebrated
with rock cut steps

demons
hills
sun stroked
thighs of sand stone

hills
demons
pelvic granite
fallen archways

demons

An Autobiography
or The Story of my Experiments with Truth

M. K. Gandhi
Translated by Mahadev Desai

Gandhi, the leading figure in the struggle for Indian independence and apostle of non-violence, published his autobiography, which he wrote in Gujarati, in 1927. Therefore it deals mainly with the earlier part of his life. Gandhi describes how, after training as a barrister in London, he returned to India to practise, but then went to South Africa to seek work as a lawyer there; the immediate motive for this was an occasion when he was insulted by an English official in India. Once in South Africa he became involved in the Indian community's struggle for basic rights and it was during this time that he worked out his ideas about non-violent protest. This passage describes what happened to him immediately after he arrived in the country. Abdullah Sheth was the Indian businessman for whom Gandhi was acting in his first case in the country.

The train reached Maritzburg, the capital of Natal, at about 9 p.m. Beddings used to be provided at this station. A railway servant came and asked me if I wanted one. 'No,' said I, 'I have one with me.' He went away. But a passenger came next, and looked me up and down. He saw that I was a 'coloured' man. This disturbed him. Out he went and came in again with one or two officials. They all kept quiet, when another official came to me and said, 'Come along, you must go to the van compartment.'

'But I have a first class ticket,' said I.

'That doesn't matter,' rejoined the other. 'I tell you, you must go to the van compartment.'

'I tell you, I was permitted to travel in this compartment at Durban, and I insist on going on in it.'

'No, you won't,' said the official. 'You must leave this compartment, or else I shall have to call a police constable to push you out.'

'Yes, you may. I refuse to get out voluntarily.'

The constable came. He took me by the hand and pushed me out. My luggage was also taken out. I refused to go to the other compartment and the train steamed away. I went and sat in the waiting room, keeping my hand-bag with me, and leaving the other luggage where it was. The railway authorities had taken charge of it.

It was winter, and winter in the higher regions of South Africa is severely cold. Maritzburg being at a high altitude, the cold was extremely bitter. My overcoat was in my luggage, but I did not dare to ask for it lest I should be insulted again, so I sat and shivered. There was no light in the room. A passenger came in at about midnight and possibly wanted to talk to me. But I was in no mood to talk.

I began to think of my duty. Should I fight for my rights or go back to India, or should I go on to Pretoria without minding the insults, and return to India after finishing the case? It would be cowardice to run back to India without fulfilling my obligation. The hardship to which I was subjected was superficial—only a symptom of the deep disease of colour prejudice. I should try, if possible, to root out the disease and suffer hardships in the process. Redress for wrongs I should seek only to the extent that would be necessary for the removal of the colour prejudice.

So I decided to take the next available train to Pretoria.

The following morning I sent a long telegram to the General Manager of the Railway and also informed Abdulla Sheth, who immediately met the General Manager. The Manager justified the conduct of the railway authorities, but informed him that he had already instructed the Station Master to see that I reached my destination safely. Abdulla Sheth wired to the Indian merchants in Maritzburg and to friends in other places to meet me and look after me. The merchants came to see me at the station and tried to comfort me by narrating their own hardships and explaining that what had happened to me was nothing unusual. They also said that Indians travelling first or second class had to expect trouble from railway officials and white passengers. The day was thus spent in listening to these tales of woe. The evening train arrived. There was a reserved berth for me. I now purchased at Maritzburg the bedding ticket I had refused to book at Durban.

The train took me to Charlestown.

More Hardships

The train reached Charlestown in the morning. There was no railway, in those days, between Charlestown and Johannesburg, but only a stage-coach, which halted at Standerton for the night *en route*. I possessed a ticket for the coach, which was not cancelled by the break of the journey at Maritzburg for a day; besides, Abdulla Sheth had sent a wire to the coach agent at Charlestown.

But the agent only needed a pretext for putting me off, and so, when he discovered me to be a stranger, he said, 'Your ticket is cancelled.' I gave him the proper reply. The reason at the back of his mind was not want of accommodation, but quite another. Passengers had to be accommodated inside the coach, but as I was regarded as a 'coolie' and looked a stranger, it would be proper, thought the 'leader', as the white man in charge of the coach was called, not to seat me with the white passengers. There were seats on either side of the coachbox. The leader sat on one of these as a rule. Today he sat inside and gave me his seat. I knew it was sheer injustice and an insult, but I thought it better to pocket it. I could not have forced myself inside, and if I had raised a protest, the coach would have gone off without me. This would have meant the loss of another day, and Heaven only knows what would have happened the next day. So, much as I fretted within myself, I prudently sat next to the coachman.

At about three o'clock the coach reached Pardekoph. Now the leader desired to sit where I was seated, as he wanted to smoke and possibly to have some fresh air. So he took a piece of dirty sackcloth from the driver, spread it on the footboard and, addressing me, said, '*Sami*, you sit on this, I want to sit near the driver.' The insult was more than I could bear. In fear and trembling I said to him, 'It was you who seated me here, though I should have been accommodated inside. I put up with the insult. Now that you want to sit outside and smoke, you would have me sit at your feet. I will not do so, but I am prepared to sit inside.'

As I was struggling through these sentences, the man came down upon me and began heavily to box my ears. He seized me by the arm and tried to drag me down. I clung to the brass rails of the coachbox and was determined to keep my hold even at the risk of breaking my wristbones. The passengers were witnessing the scene—the man swearing at me, dragging and belabouring me, and I remaining still. He was strong and I was weak. Some of the passengers were moved to pity and exclaimed: 'Man, let him alone. Don't beat him. He is not to blame. He is right. If he can't stay there, let him come and sit with us.' 'No fear,' cried the man, but he seemed somewhat crestfallen and stopped beating me. He let go my arm, swore at me a little more, and asking the Hottentot servant who was sitting on the other side of the coachbox to sit on the footboard, took the seat so vacated.

The passengers took their seats and, the whistle given, the coach rattled away. My heart was beating fast within my breast, and I was wondering whether I should ever reach my destination alive. The man cast an angry look at me now and then and, pointing his finger at me, growled: 'Take care, let me once get to Standerton and I shall show you what I do.' I sat speechless and prayed to God to help me.

After dark we reached Standerton and I heaved a sigh of relief on seeing some Indian faces. As soon as I got down, these friends said: 'We are here to receive you and take you to Isa Sheth's shop. We have had a telegram from Dada Abdulla. 'I was very glad, and we went to Sheth Isa Haji Sumar's shop. The Sheth and his clerks gathered round me. I told them all that I had gone through. They were very sorry to hear it and comforted me by relating to me their own bitter experiences.

I wanted to inform the agent of the Coach Company of the whole affair. So I wrote him a letter, narrating everything that had happened, and drawing his attention to the threat his man had held out. I also asked for an assurance that he would accommodate me with the other passengers inside the coach when we started the next morning. To which the agent replied to this effect: 'From Standerton we have a bigger coach with different men in charge. The man complained of will not be there tomorrow, and you will have a seat with the other passengers.' This somewhat relieved me. I had, of course no intention of proceeding against the man who had assaulted me, and so the chapter of the assault closed there.

In the morning Isa Sheth's man took me to the coach. I got a good seat and reached Johannesburg quite safely that night.

Standerton is a small village and Johannesburg a big city. Abdulla Sheth had wired to Johannesburg also, and given me the name and address of Muhammad Kasam Kamruddin's firm there. Their man had come to receive me at the stage, but neither did I see him nor did he recognize me. So I decided to go to a hotel. I knew the names of several. Taking a cab I asked to be driven to the Grand National Hotel. I saw the manager and asked for a room. He eyed me for a moment, and politely saying, 'I am very sorry, we are full up,' bade me good-bye. So I asked the cabman to drive to Muhammad Kasam Kamruddin's shop. Here I found Abdul Gani Sheth expecting me, and he gave me a cordial greeting. He had a hearty laugh over the story of my experience at the hotel. 'How ever did you expect to be admitted to a hotel?' he said.

'Why not?' I asked.

'You will come to know after you have stayed here a few days,' said he. 'Only *we* can live in a land like this, because, for making money, we do not mind pocketing insults, and here we are.' With this he narrated to me the story of the hardships of Indians in South Africa.

Of Sheth Abdul Gani we shall know more as we proceed.

He said: 'This country is not for men like you. Look now, you have to go to Pretoria tomorrow. You will *have* to travel third class. Conditions in the Transvaal are worse than in Natal. First and second class tickets are never issued to Indians.'

'You cannot have made persistent efforts in this direction.'

'We have sent representations, but I confess our own men too do not want as a rule to travel first or second.'

I sent for the railway regulations and read them. There was a loophole. The language of the Old Transvaal enactments was not very exact or precise; that of the railway regulations was even less so.

I said to the Sheth: 'I wish to go first class, and if I cannot, I shall prefer to take a cab to Pretoria, a matter of only thirty-seven miles.'

Sheth Abdul Gani drew my attention to the extra time and money this would mean, but agreed to my proposal to travel first, and accordingly we sent a note to the station master. I mentioned in my note that I was a barrister and that I always travelled first, I also stated in the letter that I needed to reach Pretoria as early as possible, that as there was no time to await his reply I would receive it in person at the station, and that I should expect to get a first class ticket. There was of course a purpose behind asking for the reply in person. I thought that, if the station master gave a written reply, he would certainly say 'no', especially because he would have his own notion of a 'coolie' barrister. I would therefore appear before him in fault-less English dress, talk to him and possibly persuade him to issue a first class ticket. So I went to the station in a frock-coat and necktie, placed a sovereign for my fare on the counter and asked for a first class ticket.

Wedding in the Flood

Taufiq Rafat

This poem, written in English, describes a village wedding in Pakistan that ends in tragedy.

They are taking my girl away forever,
sobs the bride's mother, as the procession
forms slowly to the whine of the clarinet.
She was the shy one. How will she fare
in that cold house, among these strangers?
This has been a long and difficult day.
The rain nearly ruined everything,
but at the crucial time, when lunch was ready,
it mercifully stopped. It is drizzling again
as they help the bride into the palankeen.
The girl has been licking too many pots.
Two sturdy lads carrying the dowry
(a cot, a looking-glass, a tin-trunk
beautifully painted in green and blue)
lead the way, followed by a foursome
bearing the palankeen on their shoulders.
Now even the stragglers are out of view.

I like the look of her hennaed hands,
gloats the bridegroom, as he glimpses
her slim fingers gripping the palankeen's side.
If only her face matches her hands
and she gives me no mother-in-law problems
I'll forgive her the cot and the trunk
and looking-glass. Will the rain never stop?
It was my luck to get a pot-licking wench.

Everything depends on the ferry-man now.
It is dark in the palankeen, thinks the bride,
and the roof is leaking. Even my feet are wet.
Not a familiar face around me
as I peep through the curtains. I'm cold and scared.
The rain will ruin cot, trunk, and looking-glass.
What sort of a man is my husband?
They would hurry, but their feet are slipping,
and there is a swollen river to cross.

They might have given a bullock at least,
grumbles the bridegroom's father; a couple of oxen
would have come in handy at the next ploughing.
Instead, we are landed with
a cot, a tin trunk, and a looking-glass,
all the things that *she* will use!
Dear God, how the rain is coming down.
The silly girl's been licking too many pots.
I did not like the look of the river
when we crossed it this morning.
Come back before three, the ferry-man said,
or you'll not find me here. I hope
he waits. We are late by an hour,
or perhaps two. But whoever heard
of a marriage party arriving on time?
The light is poor, and the paths treacherous,
but it is the river I most of all fear.

Bridegroom and bride and parents and all,
the ferry-man waits; he knows you will come,
for there is no other way to cross,
and a wedding party always pays extra.
The river is rising, so quickly aboard
with your cot, tin-trunk, and looking-glass,
that the long homeward journey can begin.
Who has seen such a brown and angry river
or can find words for the way the ferry

saws this way and that, and then disgorges
its screaming load? The clarinet fills with water.
Oh what a consummation is here;
The father tossed on the horns of the waves,
and full thirty garlands are bobbing past
the bridegroom heaved on the heaving tide,
and in an eddy, among the willows, downstream,
the coy bride is truly bedded at last.

Pratidwandi

Sunil Gangopadhyay
Translated by Enakshi Chatterjee

Pratidwandi, from which this passage is taken, is a novel written in
Bengali which tells the story of a young man from a middle-class family
in Calcutta, who has got his first degree but cannot afford to continue
his studies. His family's fortunes are in decline—they are mainly
dependent on the salary of an unmarried daughter—and Siddhartha is
desperate to get a job. In this passage we see what happens when a job
is advertised and hundreds of people apply. Chhotokaka, referred to
briefly, is an uncle. Keya is a girl Siddhartha has fallen in love with.

Mother insisted on putting some dried flowers and leaves, an
offering to the family idol, into his pocket, for good luck.
Siddhartha was not a believer, he had no time to argue with her.
He could keep them in his pocket now and throw them away. In
an effort to please his mother, he bent down and touched her
feet. Chhotokaka was talking to someone outside, so he could
not do the same to him.

He reached the place of interview some ten minutes before
nine thirty and found that it was already crowded. About three
hundred well turned out young men milled around. Some
twenty or so sat on the three benches in the verandah. The rest
stood. They were standing in the little lawn which, with its
puddles of water from last night's rain, afforded no place to sit.
All these people had come here seeking a job, but from their
looks and dress it seemed as though they had come to attend a
party.

Around ten thirty a clerk appeared and called out names to
check how many were present. Only seventeen out of the two
hundred and ninety-one persons called for the interview had
failed to turn up. It was Siddhartha's misfortune to have one

hundred and seventy-three as his serial number which meant a long period of waiting. Someone shouted to the clerk—

'You are appointing only four people, brother. Why bother to call so many?'

The man smiled smugly. 'Why ask me, brother? We are here only to obey orders!'

Another candidate said, 'Tell us something—some inside information. Have they already selected their men? Just let us know and we won't waste any more time here—'

The man looked up at the sky and thought it over. After a while he confided, 'As far as I know, they haven't. The boss is very strict. I had a candidate myself, but didn't dare put in a word.'

Above the din of the crowd, a jolly voice was heard: 'We know all your tricks. Why don't you start the game now?'

The office staff began to arrive. They cast patronizing glances at the crowd and walked in, talking confidentially among themselves. There were a few bashful women also. The interviews began at eleven.

The sun was unbearably hot. Most of the candidates had brought newspaper sheets which they held up for shade. Siddhartha had taken no such precaution. He did not mind the heat so much, but he was worried that his clothes would get soaked with perspiration and he wouldn't appear smartly dressed at the interview. He had to get this job at any cost. His legs ached as he stood there and he shifted his weight from one leg to the other continually.

Each interview took three to four minutes. How were they going to interview everybody at this rate, Siddhartha wondered. Besides, how were they going to pick out four from so many? These were all science graduates, all quite smart and healthy. From what he overheard, some of them were M.Sc.'s. Siddhartha was a little proud of his own physique but at least a dozen among them had better builds. He wondered whether he had any chance at all. Whatever happened, he had to get the job. He stood waiting patiently.

Those who were through being interviewed returned one by

one, looking confused. They tried to hide their inner apprehensions by putting on a superior smile, as if they had floored the interview board with such prompt answers that they couldn't but be offered the jobs. The first few candidates were immediately surrounded and showered with queries: What did they ask you? Something from text books? Or general knowledge? Anything from current news?

The candidate who for that moment was the centre of general attention replied disdainfully, 'Such silly questions. There's a Madrasi fellow on the Board—he thinks he is very smart. You can't even follow his English properly—'

'What did they ask? Tell us, tell us.'

'Of which country is Bonn the capital, they asked. I said Germany.'

'You said "Germany"! It should have been West Germany, shouldn't it?'

'You don't have to tell me. I told them. I gave the correct answer.'

'What else did they ask?'

'Where is Raigunj, they asked, in which district? I was figuring it out, when the Madrasi fellow cuts in: You seem to know all about Germany but don't know about Bengal! I gave it back to him straight: There are three places in Bengal with that name. Which one do you have in mind? Do you know there is a Raigunj even in Hooghly district?'

'Was all this in English? We are supposed to be posted in a village in Bengal. What good would English be to us there?'

Siddhartha felt his hands and feet grow cold. Not because of the English; he could carry on a conversation in English fairly well. But where on earth was Raigunj? He had heard the name, but he could not place it. Bankura, West Dinajpur or Maldah? Should he ask someone? But they might not ask him about Raigunj. What a mess! He had read about these places in his school geography in the lower classes but since then—yet why should they expect him to know? If the job required him to find out, he could easily consult a map, couldn't he?

As the day wore on, the interviews began getting more and

more brief. The candidates went in and came out in a minute or even less and they hurried away. Was the selection already made? It couldn't be. Siddhartha would go in and convince them how much he needed the job. He had to have it. He had all the qualifications and he would work very hard. There were others just as well qualified too, but his need was the greatest. The sun grew so hot that he couldn't stand any more. They should have made arrangements for seating all these people they had called. He always felt hungry when he stayed away from home for long. He had smoked a number of cigarettes, because others were smoking. It made him feel light and empty inside. He felt that all the mechanism inside his stomach had disappeared, leaving behind a void.

At one o'clock, a half-hour break was announced. The members of the Board were to have their lunch. Siddhartha crossed over to the other side of the road and went to a street vendor for a snack. He was tempted to go away for a couple of hours, but he did not dare. He had a faint hope he might be called even before his turn. His application would so impress them that they might want to give him the job right away.

A young man who stammered slightly had also come to the snacks vendor. Siddhartha talked with him, suppressing an impulse to laugh at the other's speech defect. He took it for granted that this boy wouldn't succeed. With his stammer, he hardly stood a chance among so many others.

But as he talked to the boy, Siddhartha felt sympathetic towards him. He looked very innocent and rather sad. Why should he not get a job? Just because he stammered? That was most unfair. When Siddhartha heard about this boy's family, he felt worse. He had enrolled for the M.Sc. classes, but gave up because the family could not afford it. They were seven brothers and sisters. Their father was ill, and one sister was a widow with two children. They had not been able to pay the house rent for five months. He had taken up private tuition, but it was not very successful because the pupils couldn't help laughing. He had even tried getting a school teaching job. Siddhartha felt that this boy needed a job more than he did. After all, his own family didn't have to pay house rent. Apart from what his sister earned, they got some royalties from Father's old company. But this boy had nothing.

In spite of his condition the boy offered to pay for the snacks. This offer moved Siddhartha deeply. He stopped the other boy from paying and paid for both of them himself. He wondered, if he did get the job after all should he let this boy have it? But that wasn't possible under the circumstances. 'Have you ever appeared for an interview like this before?' he asked.

The young man smiled: 'Haven't I? The number of ap-apapplications I have sent! You know what a fr-fr-friend tells me! Get three hundred applications pri-pri-printed, instead of getting them ty-ty-typed every time, keeping a little spa-spa-space on top.'

'What do they ask you at an interview?'

'What can they ask? Nobody wants to tell a fellow who stam-stam-stammers that he is a stam-stam-stammerer to his face. But it's all lu-lu-luck, you know.'

A car whizzed past and Siddhartha's heart gave a lurch. Was it Tultul? Yes, it was, along with a few other girls, Chhotomashi and yes, there was Keya, too. Tultul waved, but the car did not stop. She said something to Keya and Keya turned around to look. Could she see him? Siddhartha pretended that he was waiting for a bus.

A hum of discontent arose from the crowd in the afternoon. It was three o'clock already and only about a hundred interviews had taken place. It would be eight or nine in the evening before they would all be done. They had been standing from nine in the morning. All those lively faces seen in the morning had lost their sparkle through the hot, perspiring day. It was impossible to stand on the grass strip out in the open and everybody had crowded into the corridor. But there were no fans here.

With so many young people present, there was a constant buzz of conversation. Whenever the noise grew in volume, a bell clanged and two Bhojpuri darwans appeared. 'Aaplog aisa chillanessey, saheb bolta, sab bandh ho jayga. Ekdam chup kijiyey. Mu mat kholna,' they warned.

There was a crowd in front of the room in which the interviews were being held. The two darwans pushed the candidates away from time to time. They were getting impatient, these young men—they were becoming increasingly aware of the fact that there were only four vacancies to be filled.

Siddhartha exercised patience with great effort, but his face was like that of a person who has been profoundly humiliated. He heard indignant voices around him: 'What do the bastards think they are doing? Five rupees they took in postal orders from all of us. No travelling allowance and we have to eat lunch at our own expense. And not even a place to sit—'

'While we are roasting, they are having a nice time under the fan.'

'How much longer now?'

'I know their sort, after five they'll ask the rest of us to come tomorrow.'

'Not again! And spend good money in coming all the way! They won't pay for the transport either, the bloodsuckers.'

'Why don't they tell us that they've got their own men for these posts?'

'They are just going in and coming out. What kind of interview is this?'

'Probably they're looking at faces. Are they homos?'

'A lottery would have been the best thing.'

'One should chuck a bomb at them.'

Siddhartha did not join them, but as he listened to them his inner agitation steadily grew. In spite of himself, the familiar symptoms appeared—quickened breathing, hairs on end, eyes smarting at the corners. At such times, his body was the only weapon which he could hurl against any obstacle. He had a strong desire to kick the door open, break off an arm from a chair, and square up for a fight. This kind of thought was painful to him, for he badly wanted the job—though the chances now seemed very slim indeed.

The growing resentment reached a critical point as another break was announced. A bearer carried in a tea-tray for the bosses. By now it was unbearably hot outside. Everybody's

78

carefully washed and ironed shirts were soaking wet. Most of them unbuttoned their shirts and fanned themselves with their handkerchiefs.

The first explosion occurred over the right to occupy the few benches on the corridor. There were three benches on which about eighteen boys were squeezed. Another batch went up to them and demanded, 'You have rested long enough, it's our turn now.' About forty others rushed up to the benches but those who were in occupation refused to vacate. Angry words first, then some mutual pushing, but before actual blows were exchanged someone had the good sense to cry out, 'Why fight among ourselves? There are only three benches after all. Let us ask them to provide more seats. They've got to.' Some backed away, others came forward, Siddhartha among them. He went up to the interview room, opened the door and asked politely, 'May we come in, sir?'

Three elderly gentlemen wearing suits and ties were sitting around a large circular table and chatting amiably over cups of tea. All of them looked up in great surprise at the intruders and stared at them for a while. Then one member of the interview board said, 'Not just now, a little later—you'll be called.'

Siddhartha said, 'It is something else that we came to see you about, sir.'

'Not now, not now, later.'

None of the three moved their hands but probably pressed a foot switch, for the bell buzzed again. At once the two darwans entered and began pushing the boys out of the room. They drew back at first, but one of the taller fellows protested: 'What's this, treating us like cats and dogs! Being pushed around by darwans! Let's go back and give them a bit of our minds—.' A fat chap agreed: 'Of course, they're obliged to give us seats. We sent good money with our applications. If these darwans misbehave again—'

They surged forward, pushed the darwans out of the way, and entered again: 'Sir, we have been standing for the last six hours. Couldn't we get some place to sit down?'

One of the three members got up and came towards them.

Siddhartha looked at him straight in the face. The gentleman asked, 'What is it?'

'Sir, we've been standing for hours, there's no place to sit—'

The gentleman smiled sweetly: 'You have to prepare for much worse in this job. If you can't bear this, well, then, I'm sorry for you, young man—'

'Sir, we can do some work standing, but we can't just stand around doing nothing!'

'Didn't I say—if you can't bear this, you're free to—'

'I'm speaking for all of us—'

But just as he said this Siddhartha realized that the rest of the boys had fled, leaving him alone to face the gentleman. He was the only rebel. The gentleman beamed at him: 'All right, let me have your serial number. If you find this too inconvenient, we can send for you earlier.'

Siddhartha felt scared, because he realized that his own chances of getting the job were receding. But out of this fear came the defiance with which he replied, 'I'm not speaking for myself, sir, I don't want any special favour.'

The gentleman spoke with abrupt sharpness and change of tone, 'Then get back, and wait your turn quietly. Don't make any more trouble.'

He banged the door in Siddhartha's face. Useless anger welled up within Siddhartha and he began to feel a vague pain in his chest.

The crowd, subdued for the time being, now began to hum again. The young man who stammered came up to Siddhartha and said in a sympathetic tone, 'Why did you volunteer, brother? They will remember your face.' Others said, 'You've ruined your chances. What's the sense in going in for your interview now? If you can speak back to them like this even before getting the job, they're bound to think you will start organizing unions and protests when you get the job. You were right, of course, in protesting, but when you've to work under them you must suck up to them.'

Siddhartha looked about him wildly. The tall fellow and the fat chap were nowhere around. He shouted in an unnatural voice, 'The hell with your job. I piss on it. You think I'll starve if I don't get this job?'

He rushed to the door and shoved it open. Standing there in a defiant posture, he shouted, 'You can't get away with these rotten tricks much longer. Keeping all these decent fellows out in the heat and yourself—you fatbellied swine, you sons of bitches—'

The bell screeched desperately. Before the darwans could lay their hands on him, Siddhartha pushed one of them to the ground and ran. He cleared his way through the crowd and ran like mad past the corridor, across the lawn, out in the street. On the other side he stopped and looked back to see if anyone had followed. No, nobody had. Panting, he glared at the building, mumbling to himself, 'I'll come back here. You bet I will. I'll come and get you all, every bloody son of a bitch. See if I don't.'

Chowringhee was full of the afternoon bustle. Trams, buses, motor cars rushed along. Some people crossed the street idly. Nobody bothered to notice Siddhartha. He stood still for some time, fuming and helpless. The corners of his eyes smarted, his fingertips burned, his breath seemed to be on fire, his face felt as if blood would burst from it any moment. He was unable to think of what he should do next. Oh, if he could lay his hands on a machine-gun. He would kneel down and open fire, rat-tat-tat—destroying everything, blow that building to bits, shoot each of them like cattle—. But no, there was nothing he could do except stare at the building. There were so many people on the street but no one cared to know what had happened to Siddhartha.

Back home, he did not change his clothes. He took off only his shoes and socks and stretched out on the bed. The afternoon was ebbing away and the corners of the room were growing dark. The cheerful noise of boys flying kites came through the window. He turned over and pressed his face into his pillow, feeling miserable and close to tears. His chest was full of heaviness, he wished he could cry. But he couldn't, probably because he had forgotten how to. Instead, tired out by the day's exhaustion, he fell asleep.

Presently Mother came and woke him up: 'Binu, why are you

sleeping at this time of the day? How was your interview?'

He looked up at Mother sleepily and suddenly felt very sorry for her. After a long time he was once again aware that Mother was the only person in the world who really cared for him. How could he bear to make her sad, she was so eager for good news. He made up his mind immediately. He sat up and said cheerfully, 'It was wonderful, Ma. It's almost sure. They've all but promised. The appointment letter should come any time next week.' Then he saw someone in a sari on the verandah, realized it was Sutapa, and raised his voice: 'You know something, Ma? It adds up to four hundred and ten rupees, not including first class TA for tours. It's a very good job.' Before Mother could ask any questions, he quickly added, 'I've got to go out now.'

Master Babu

Kaiser Haq

In this poem, written in English, Kaiser Haq evokes the sad figure of the English teacher, obliged to give private lessons in order to eke out an inadequate salary.

He doesn't talk, he converses
or (better still) engages in conversation.
If his pupils indulge in it in class
He doesn't ask them to shut up or keep quiet
But to maintain silence,
Which, he maintains, is golden,
And in a torrent of words explains why.

Dog-eared as the edition of *Nesfield's Grammar*
Clutched in one hand, he walks home
At day's end through fetid streets
Jostled by other people's cares,

Partakes of a repast of rice and *dal*
Before an evening of private tuition:
Making the rounds like a GP, dispensing
Extra doses of parts of speech to those
With faulty powers of assimilation.
It makes both ends of the day
Meet at dinner. But, 'Where's your son?'
The mother can't answer.

He ambles in at dinner's end.
'Where have you been, may I ask, if you allow
It is not presumptuous of me to do so.

I see you have the impertinence to maintain silence.
When will you begin to partially
Shoulder family responsibility?'
The mother starts to sob.
Howlers appear—
'Stop you from crying,
I am conversing him on crucial thing'—
And multiply . . .
But midnight imposes a kind of resolution;
He goes to bed mumbling to himself—
As if it were a balm—words in the acquired
Foreign tongue, his precious bread—without—butter.

At times freedom from care does come to him,
Like an empty paper bag blown down the street
That snatches at the legs, touches a moment, and is gone.

Circus Cat Alley Cat

Anita Desai

In this short story, written in English, the author shows how an apparently everyday character assumes a special significance for a child.

I first saw Anna, the new 'nanny' of the English children who lived next door, in a pink stucco house, late one evening when she came to hound us out of the shrubbery where we were playing hide-and-seek, a game which, as anyone knows, grows exciting only at dinnertime. I crept behind a screen of bamboos and peered out at her through the polished bars of the bamboo stalks. She was large and heavily built, with very black bright eyes and a lot of wiry black hair. She bent down to pick up a neem switch and slapped it against her thigh as she called to us in a loud, sharp voice. And through the cage of bamboos, in that blue twilight, I saw the lawn turn to a sawdust covered stage floor and Nanny's white uniform into spangled pink tights and the switch in her hand to a long, whistling whip that cracked in the air which was filled no longer with the talking of mynah birds and the barks of pet dogs, but with the roars of tigers and the gibbering of apes. Sick with terror, I found I could scarcely breathe and preferred to creep over the manure pit to my own home than on to the lawn and face to face with Nanny.

My imagination was fired, no doubt, as much by the fact that I had only that morning heard that Nanny came from a circus where she had worked as cat-trainer, as by the cracking of the switch in her hand and her hefty shoulders and authoritative voice. How the staid, plain, and entirely unimaginative family of Bates could choose a circus performer to be a Nanny for their children is an eternal mystery, though they endeavoured to explain it to us as an act of charity. Anna, they told us (her real

85

name, or stage name, was Shakti—Strength! Power!—but the Bateses preferred to call her by the more tame and domestic name of Anna) was a Malabar girl who had been born into the circus, and had trained the big cats since she was thirteen. Her special 'breath-taking, death-defying, terror-striking' act was to drape a tiger over her shoulders and stand on the backs of two lions whom she would then order to emit great, rumbling roars that made her large frame tremble all over and the tiger snarl. Dressed in parrot-green tights and a lilac shirt with silver spangles, her fierce mane of hair standing on end, she must have looked a sight. Then she married the boy who fed the cats. The boy was ambitious. In no time, he had taught her that a woman's place is her home and was straddling the lions himself and wrapping the tiger round his own neck. Anna, in a spurt of cat-like temper, left. By that time she had a baby, and when Mrs Bates found her, she and the child were near starvation, begging on a Daryaganj street. Mrs Bates gave her a white uniform and put bath-salts in her tub in order to wash off that special circus odour of elephant manure and cat sweat; she was installed as the children's Nanny, and her baby put in a cradle on the back verandah and fed on milk and oranges.

All this played real havoc on our imagination, as nothing had ever done before. She had only to rattle the knobs of the windows and doors as she banged them shut against the summer heat, to make us feel we were being shut into our cages. We would no longer walk, or run, but prowl. We would not hop or skip, but spring and leap. Even our voices changed. Anna had only to come into the room with a tricycle or our skipping-ropes, and we would feel the trainer had arrived, wooden chair in hand, to practise the act, and in this spirit we would play the games she ordered us to play. Anna had only to sit down at the breakfast table and cut the bread into slices for us, to make us think of it as a great hunk of fresh meat, dripping with scarlet blood, and we would shudder as we gnawed at it. A cooking-spoon in Anna's hand would become a biting, snapping, snaky whip. A plain brooch pinned in her lapel would change the plain white uniform to a gaudy, satin stage costume. When the lights were switched on at night, the brightness of Anna's eyes was the brightness of a stage-performer's eyes in the glare of white-hot arc lamps. No matter how hard Mrs Bates tried to domesticate her and turn her into a tame alley-cat, a nice, motherly pussy-cat, Anna remained to us the 'breath-taking death-defying, terror-striking' Anna of the circus. Poor Anna herself played no part in this. No matter how hard we tried, and how cleverly, she never spoke of the circus once. Yet the very house, with its Rangoon creeper, its worn rugs and nursery pictures, became the Big Top for us, the dinner-bell, the big drums, the lights, the spotlights of the stage. We lived in a constant quiver of thrill upon thrill. I dreamt of cats all the night, long-striped cats leaping in the air, great cats shaking their manes as they roared, their muscles rippling under the smooth skin, the shining hair. They sprang soundlessly from dream to dream, landing softly on my eyelids, and from strangers of the jungle they became companions of the long nights of excitement.

And then Anna's baby vanished. I came across Anna in the garden one day, her hair more disordered than ever, her eyes red from weeping. 'My baby's gone!' she cried theatrically, 'My baby's been taken away. Oh God, oh God, give my baby back to me—but I'll never see her again—she's been taken away from me.' And I joined wholeheartedly in the weeping to think that God had taken the child at such a tender age and left poor Anna all alone. As I ran back to the house to tell my mother, I wondered if the baby had suddenly been taken ill, because she had seemed very healthy and well only the previous day. My mother was, for this reason, equally shocked and immediately went to see Anna.

Anna wept on her shoulders, looking quite thin and pathetic in her sorrow. My mother pressed her hand and soothed her, 'What God decrees, we must accept Anna. It is sad but it must be, Anna.' On her way out, she looked in on Mrs Bates, and asked, 'When is the funeral to be?'

'The funeral?' Mrs Bates jumped. 'What funeral?'

'Why, of poor Anna's baby!'

'Anna's baby? Why, is it dead?'

We were nonplussed that the mistress of the house should not have heard of the tragedy yet. My mother and I interrupted each other in trying to tell her what had happened and were horrified when the kind old missionary's wife chortled and clapped her hand over her mouth to stop her laughter.

'The baby dead!' she cried. 'Whatever gave you the idea? It's only that Anna's husband and his family came and took it away. We're trying to get it back, only the circus has moved to Bombay now so it will be a bit difficult. We're sending Anna off to try though.'

That was the last we saw of Anna for a long time. The next time was several years later when we went to see a circus and found Shakti's name on the handbill, and a picture of Anna with a snarling tiger on her shoulders. She was smiling hugely.

We could scarcely wait till she appeared and then were so excited we could not even applaud. We watched out for her baby and wondered if it had grown into the little girl who was somersaulting in the sawdust and tumbling around with a deeply preoccupied expression on her thin face. But throughout the performance, the thought uppermost in my mind was: where is Anna's husband? And I had a vivid picture of Anna in a great cage, gnawing, gnawing upon a great, bleeding hunk of flesh, Anna snarling at the people who came to snatch it from her, Anna throwing back her mane and giving a great roar of triumph, Anna the queen of the circus cats, Anna the circus cat . . .

Of Mothers, among other things
and Self-Portrait

A. K. Ramanujan

Two poems by a well-known contemporary poet who writes poetry in English.

Of Mothers, among other things

I smell upon this twisted
blackbone tree the silk and white
petal of my mother's youth.
From her ear-rings three diamonds

splash a handful of needles,
and I see my mother run back
from rain to the crying cradles.
The rains tack and sew

with broken thread the rags
of the tree-tasselled light.
But her hands are a wet eagle's
two black pink-crinkled feet,

One talon crippled in a garden—
trap set for a mouse. Her sarees
do not cling: they hang, loose
feather of a onetime wing.

My cold parchment tongue licks bark
in the mouth when I see her four
still sensible fingers slowly flex
to pick up a grain of rice from the kitchen floor.

Self-Portrait

I resemble everyone
but myself, and sometimes see
in shop-windows,
    despite the well-known laws
    of optics,
the portrait of a stranger,
date unknown,
often signed in a corner
by my father.

Roots and Shadows

Shashi Deshpande

Indu, the first-person narrator in these two extracts from the English-language novel *Roots and Shadows*, has grown up in her extended family but has now moved away. She is married and has a career as a journalist. When the story opens Akka, the old lady who ruled the family with a rod of iron, has just died and it is found that she has left her money to Indu. Indu now holds the family's destinies in her hands and has to decide whether she should sell the house and use the money to finance Mini's marriage (Mini is her niece), or spend the money on maintaining the family home. In the first passage, the sale of the house is being discussed. Madhav-kaka and Vinayak-kaka are uncles. Shyamro is not a family member; he is acting as a go-between and Shankarappa is the prospective purchaser. The second passage takes the discussion a stage further when Indu sounds out Mini about the prospective marriage.

1

'Yes, it is a good offer.' Madhav-kaka agreed.

'We should snap it up. What are we waiting for?' Sumant asked.

'Yes, yes, I know. Snap it up. Snap it up.' Kaka glared about him. 'Sell it to him. Let him demolish the house. What do we care about as long as we get our share of the money? And what about us old people? What are we supposed to do? Lie down by the roadside and die? Or will someone put us in the cattle pound? Or sell us to the butchers? Who cares? Yes, sell it, sell it.'

While all of us stared at him aghast, Kaka buried his face in his dhoti and gave a fierce honk.

'Who's Shankarappa? And what's all this about selling the house? Will no one tell me?'

For once I blessed Father's naïvety. While Shyamrao told

Father all about it in his flat, unemotional tone, Kaka recovered himself. He cleared his throat and looked about him in a shame-faced manner. As he caught my eye, he gave me an abashed smile. But I didn't respond. I couldn't. For the first time, I had realized something. I looked at the long narrow room, with its polished floor, its arched windows through which the sunlight streamed in. I saw, as if for the first time, the niches in the walls full of odds and ends, the pegs on the wall on which the men had once hung their turbans and now their caps and coats and folded dhotis. Demolished. It would cease to exist.

Would it? The wall would crumble, the roof would crash down. The woodwork would be neatly piled up in lorries and carried away. But what of the feelings, the emotions, the passions the house had sheltered? Would they not linger here, where they had had their birth, their life? If not, where would they go? I had been a fifteen-days-old motherless infant when I had been brought into this house. I had lived eighteen years in it. Now, all these eighteen years compressed themselves into one moment of painful intensity and I lived those eighteen years all over again.

The enchantment of waking up in the morning to various sounds that somehow formed a harmonious whole. Birds chirping in the windows. A child crying. (Sometimes the child was me.) The Primus hissing. The tinkle of cups and saucers. Akka singing. And then, the magic of the evening hours, when the first lamp was lit for the gods. The lights gently twinkling in all the rooms. Women sitting at ease for the first time in the day, stretching out their aching legs in front of them. Story-telling-time ... children lying with heads pillowed on warm laps, listening with a drowsy intentness, when the whole didn't matter, but each word was significant and meaningful. Men returning home, shedding their slippers, washing their feet, and settling down with large contented sighs. The feeling of ease, content, and indolence embracing the whole house. And the huge front door, which no child could ever push the whole way, standing wide open the whole day, so that people just walked in and became part of the family. A feeling of welcome that didn't have to be said in words, smiles, dinners, and drinks. This was home. Where one lived. Not stayed.

And suddenly I was back in the present, surrounded by the buzz of angry voices.

'It's our home. Grandfather built it. Can't we make some sacrifices for it?'

'Are you prepared to make the sacrifice?'

'Yes, as much as I can. But how much can one person do?'

'It's easy for you. You have no responsibilities. Let me be frank. I can't spare anything.'

'And why not sell the house when we can get a good price for it?'

'I agree. It's foolishness to miss this chance.'

'Yes, yes, I'm a foolish old man. Put me in an asylum and do what you want.'

It was Madhav-kaka's voice that finally pierced through my stupor.

'Well, Indu, why are you so silent? You're the most important person here. We're all waiting for your decision. You must tell us what it is.'

I looked at them all . . . Madhav-kaka faintly mocking. Vinayak-kaka hostile, Kaka trying hard to keep the appeal out of his eyes, Father troubled and anxious for me. What could I say? 'What can I do?' I turned in relief to Shyamrao, whose face was blank and impersonal. 'Can I buy the house myself? And maintain it as well?'

'You could.' He looked doubtfully at me. 'But if you did, you would have to pay at least what Shankarappa is offering. Which means . . . yes, I doubt if you could finance Padmini's marriage as well.'

'Mini's marriage . . . that's settled, is it? You're all agreed that Mini should marry that man?'

'Why not?' Vinayak-kaka gave me an owlish look through his glasses.

'Yes, why not? The perfect couple. So say the horoscopes.'

'No.' It was Madhav-kaka. 'Not perfect. But what couple could be perfectly matched? Tell me, Indu . . . you choose your own husband. Are you a made-for-each-other couple?' He enunciated the words as if making a burlesque of them, making them sound what they were . . . ridiculous.

But I . . . I could not speak. If only I had the talons of a bird, the claws of a tiger, the poison of a cobra . . .

'Madhav,' Father put his hand on mine, 'you know what Indu really means.'

'And what does she mean? Tell me, Indu?'

All heads swivelled to me. I had to gain control over myself. I couldn't show the cracks in my armour. I had to speak. Show no weakness . . . wasn't that how Akka had ruled? But did I need Akka's methods?

'You people . . . you've thought of everything . . . the families, the communities, the stars, the gotras, everything . . .'

'Yes, is that wrong, Indu? Madhav-kaka interrupted me. 'Marriage itself is a difficult enough business. For two people to merge into one identity, it's . . . almost an impossibility. But given certain things in common . . . language, customs, rituals, background . . . all this makes it easier.'

'2 + 2 makes 4.'

'Yes, 2 + 2 does make 4. I don't know why you intellectuals,' he smiled and I thought . . . I wouldn't like to be his subordinate, 'disdain that equation.'

They were all watching us as if it was a duel.

'Oh, that equation is fine for Maths. But not for humans, Madhav-kaka. You're leaving out that great incalculable . . . human emotions.'

2

She wrung her hair out like a wet cloth and drops of water fell on the cement floor. It was so heated that the drops sizzled and evaporated in a moment. I shaded my eyes against the glare, while Mini who had been up here longer, merely screwed up her eyes.

'But not here. It's too hot. Let's go down.'

Obediently she followed me, stopping once at the door to say, 'You remember, Indu, how we used to come up here for the champak flowers? And how brave you were, walking on the parapet, leaning forwards to pluck the flowers?'

I laughed. 'Showing off! Just showing off. I liked to imagine myself a daredevil. I used to be scared to death really. But I could never reveal that.'

'And Indu,' Mini went on chattily as we walked down the cool, dark stairs, 'the funniest thing was that you never liked the flowers at all. You always gave them to me.'

'Did I?'

I stopped and stared at her, seeing her as a small child, her small dark face blazing with pleasure as I gave her the flowers. 'Yes, now I remember it. But Mini, where are you going? I said I want to talk to you.'

'I suddenly remembered something myself. Kaka wanted me to cut up some supari for him. And I forgot all about it. I'd better do it now before he starts shouting at Mother for his supari.'

We went downstairs into what was technically Kaki's room. It hadn't changed in all the years since my childhood. The same ancient cupboards of dark wood, the same trunks piled up in a corner, the same photographs lined up on the wall. Mini pulled down a large brass tin. 'Here's the supari. Where are the nutcrackers?'

As she rummaged in the shelves, I held my breath. And then she emerged with the same brass nutcrackers I had seen as a child. I laughed aloud. Mini stared at me in surprise. 'What?'

'Nothing. Is there another pair, Mini? Can I help you?'

Now she giggled. 'Another pair? I was lucky to find this one. But you can dry the paan for Kaka. Here . . .' She brought out a flat brass tin. 'And here . . .' she poked in the cupboard again, '. . . a towel to wipe the paan.'

And so, there we were, the two of us doing what I had done so many times as a child. Miraculously the technique came back and I was as expert and brisk as if I had never given off doing it. Place the towel on your lap, wipe the paan once this way, once the other side . . . and into the box. And Mini snipped snipped away industriously at the supari until a small brown mound grew between us.

'Do you know, Mini,' I said after a silence, 'that there are some workers in industries who spend a whole working life doing the same small bit of work over and over again? Just that and nothing else. Imagine you're a worker in a car factory. Your job is drilling some holes in a metal sheet. And you do just that and nothing else all your life. You never even get to see the car of which your sheet is a part. What do you think you'd feel when you were dying and trying to sum up your life?'

Mini tittered, covering her mouth with the end of her sari to hide her uneven teeth.

'You think the most peculiar thoughts, Indu. What's the point of thinking of such things?'

'The point . . .? You mean, you never think unless there is?' She shook her head, giving me a scared look as if she knew what was coming.

'What about your marriage? Is that one of the things there's no point in thinking of?'

'Why should I think of it? I'm past 24. I have to get married. What else is there to think about?'

'But Mini . . . marriage is . . . It means living with a man. You have to listen to him, endure his habits, his smell, his touch, his likes, his dislikes. You have to sleep with him, bear him children. Can you do all that with this man?' She put the nutcrackers down gently, and picking up her still wet hair, knotted it at the base of her neck. Mini's palms had two red lines where the nutcrackers had cut into them. I lifted the nutcrackers. They were heavy. Mini loosened my fingers and took the nutcrackers back from me.

'What choice have I, Indu?' she asked me, resuming her snipping. Snip snip . . . the supari fell between us. Millions of girls had asked this question millions of times in the country. Surely it was time they stopped asking it? What choice have I? Surely it is this, this fact that I can choose, that differentiates me from the animals. But years of blindfolding can obscure your vision so that you no more see the choices. Years of shackling can hamper your movement so that you can no more move out of your cage of no-choices.

'But Mini, are you getting married because there's nothing else you can do?'

'Of course.' She gave me a petulant look. 'Look, I've jammed my finger.'

And so she had.

'Leave it alone for some time.'

She watched her finger where the blood was forming an angry red clot under the skin. She licked at it like a child.

'Leave it alone, Mini.'

Obediently she put her hands in her lap.

'And you didn't answer my question.'

'Of course I'm marrying him because there's nothing else I can do. I'm no good at studies. I never was. I went to school because . . . I had to. And then to college because Akka said I must go. Boys prefer graduates these days, she said. So I went. But I failed and it was a relief to give it up. There's only one thing I'm really good at . . . looking after a home. And to get a home, I have to get married. This is not my home, is it?'

'Isn't it?'

'You know it isn't. Ever since we were small, we were told . . . "You'll be going away one day to your own home." They said it to you and me, never to Hemant or Sumant or Sharad or Sunil.'

'But Mini, will any man do? Doesn't it matter who he is?'

'I'd better get on with this. Mother will be angry with me if Kaka asks for supari before I finish. Any man, Indu? Yes, any man. Any man who says "yes". You don't know what it has been like. Watching Kaka and Hemant and even Madhav-kaka running around after eligible men. And then, sending the horoscope and having it come back with a message. "It doesn't match". And if the horoscopes matched, there was the meeting to be arranged. And Mother and Atya slogging in the kitchen the whole day. And all those people coming and . . . staring and asking all kinds of questions. And if we heard they were old-fashioned people, I would dress up in an old-fashioned manner and they would say, "She's not modern enough." And if I dressed up well because someone said the boy wanted a smart wife, they would say, "She's too fashionable for us." Or too short. Or too tall. Or too dark. Or something. And Kaka trying to laugh and talk to those people, while his eyes looked so . . . anxious. And I, feeling as if I had committed a great crime by being born a girl. To make your parents look like that . . . And then, they would say, someone else in the family wants to see the girl. So we would have to go through with it all over again. And finally, if everything was fine, there was the dowry. You know nothing of this, Indu. You're lucky. You escaped all this. And now, when someone has agreed, can I refuse and make Kaka go through all of it all over again? Just because the man isn't . . .'

'Isn't what?' I asked, after waiting for her to complete her sentence.

'Oh, I don't know. And I don't care. He'll look after me. And no one can say to me, "How old are you? And not married yet! What a pity!" I'm tired, Indu. I don't care what kind of a man he is. Once we are married, and he becomes my husband, none of his faults will matter.'

The Indian way. The husband. A definite article. Permanent. Not only for now, but for ever. To be accepted. Stop.

'Marriage as a catalyst, eh?'

I said the words in English and Mini stared at me blankly. 'What does that mean, Indu?' she asked naïvely. 'I've forgotten all the English I learnt in school. You were always so good at it. Now you even talk in your sleep in English. Last night you were saying . . .'

'Yes?' I felt a tremor within me.

'In English . . .' she said accusingly, as if pinpointing my crime.

'But what?' I asked impatiently.

'Oh, something very funny. Something like . . .' she switched over to her thickly accented English '. . . "it's not fair. It's not fair."'

Not fair. Not fair. Odd how one relives bits of one's life in one's sleep. But, why that moment and why that phrase? I could recall it so distinctly. Jayant and I at the end of one of our moments of love. And I, aghast at my total self-abandonment, had cried out, 'It's not fair.' I tried to push away the thoughts and images. Mini was looking curiously at me.

'So you want to marry him, Mini?'

'Yes,' she said with an unexpected firmness. Then, as if frightened by her own temerity, appealingly, 'If you agree.'

'You mean if I pay.'

'It's the same thing.'

Breaking Stones

Nirala
Translated by David Rubin

Translated from the Hindi, this poem is by a leading modern poet who
died in 1961.

A woman breaking stones—
on a road near Allahabad I saw her
breaking stones.

No shade
from the tree under which she sat.
Her body black, her young breasts
bound tight in the *choli*;
eyes lowered,
mind turned to her lover
and acts of love.
The heavy hammer in her hand
struck time and time again.
Across the road long rows of trees
and high-walled mansions.
It was the hottest season,
the sun glaring,
and the scorching wind rose,
burning the earth like cotton,
with the air full of dust and sparks.
    It was noon by now,
      and she still breaking stones.
While I watched she saw me,
looked at me once,
then at the house, then at her ragged clothes.

Seeing no one else was there
she stared at me with the eyes
of one who doesn't cry
even when they beat her.
As from a tuned sitar
I heard a strain of music then
I'd never heard before.
After a moment she shuddered,
beautiful,
while the sweat trickled down her forehead,
then once more gave herself to the work
as though to say,
     'I'm a woman
     breaking stones'.

The Only American from our Village

Arun Joshi

This short story, written in English, describes what happens when Dr Khanna, an Indian scientist who has settled in America, returns to India for a visit. The court paper sold by the *ashtamp farosh* who tells the story of what happened to Dr Khanna's father is special stamped paper on which certain legal documents are required to be written.

Dr Khanna was easily the most outstanding immigrant physicist at the University of Wisconsin. Personally, he considered himself to be the finest of *all* physicists, immigrant or native. He was also among the dozen or so best-dressed men on the campus.

When he was forty Dr Khanna, his wife Joanne, and their two sons decided to visit India, the country that Dr Khanna had left fifteen years earlier and where his fame had preceded him.

The four week trip was a success by all accounts. He was received by an official of the Council of Scientific Research. He addressed a conference on Interplanetary radiation and inaugurated three well-attended seminars. He met the President and the Prime Minister. He was offered many jobs each of which he politely declined.

His wife and children were worshipped by his relatives whom they had never met before and for whom they had brought Gillette razors, pop records, and a mass of one-dollar neck-ties. The records and the neck-ties were unusable because the relatives had neither record-players nor suits but the razors were greatly prized, especially by the women who saved them for their teenaged sons.

The last of the four weeks Mrs Khanna and the children went off on a sightseeing tour. Dr Khanna delivered his final talk at a college in his former home-town.

The talk went well. He was introduced to the audience in glorious terms and the boys stayed quiet which was not natural for them. He was thanked profusely and, it seemed, endlessly by the lecturer in Physics. Some of the audience stopped by on their way out and bid their humble farewell with folded hands. At the end of them all an old man came shuffling along and insisted on shaking Dr Khanna's hands.

'I am the *ashtamp farosh* of the town,' the old man said, staring up at Dr Khanna. His eyes were heavy with cataract. The grease on his jacket shone in the yellow light. Dr Khanna looked on, puzzled. The Principal was embarrassed.

'Mr Radhey Mohan', he explained, 'sells court paper in front of the District Courts.'

'Yes,' the old man repeated. 'I am the *ashtamp farosh* of the town. I knew your father. I am very happy to see you. I came here only to see you because I am only an *ashtamp farosh* and do not understand such matters. Nor do my sons because they are not even matriculates. I have not been out of this town. I live in the village which was also your father's village and is, therefore, *your* village. Ha! Ha! I can take you there if you like.'

'I had been to our village when I was a boy,' said Dr Khanna hastily. He was glad he could say that because some trick of the old man, a slant of the lips, a glint in the eye, the accent, which had also been his father's, had made him uncomfortable. 'I have been to our village several times,' he repeated.

'I know. When you came with your father, you always came to my house because your father and I were very close to each other, like brothers, and I was not then the *ashtamp farosh* because I had property and I did not have to be an *ashtamp farosh* and I lived in style. Of course, all this does not interest you. I know that.'

There was a pause. The Principal who had been trying to put an end to this unexpected encounter edged Dr Khanna towards the door. The *ashtamp farosh* put his hand on Dr Khanna's shoulder and began again. Darkness gathered on the grounds outside.

'He was a good student, the best. I sat at the same desk, so I know. I carved my name on my side of the desk. Your father did not want to spoil the wood so I carved his name on *his* side. Before he died we went and looked for the desk and, believe me, it was still there. So were the names. It was very strange. I had not expected the names to be there. Your father's name is on the Honours Board, too. Mine is not there, because I failed in matriculation. But his name is there. If you like we can go and have a look. He stood third in the state. Maybe you don't know it. Standing third in forty thousand boys was no joke. He won a scholarship as he always did. He wanted to take up a job but his mother said he must go to college. So he went to Lahore. I am told he made a mark there. But I don't know. I saw him only when he came home for vacation. If he had made a mark he did not let it get to his head. He was always the same with me. I wanted to know about the dancing girls of Lahore but he did not know about such things. But he had brains. Even I could see that. I met him every summer, several summers running. Then he took a job somewhere. In Lucknow or Kanpur or Alla-habad—I don't know. You must know better. I saw him when his mother died. He cried a lot. Then he locked up the old house and went away. I did not see much of him for twenty years. Only once or twice when he brought you and your sisters to see the village. He came back after he retired. He looked old, older than his years, but he was happy. He was very proud of you. He told everyone what all you had done. He got angry with me because I was not interested in what you had done. He used to say you would be a big government man when you came back. He would say you were coming back in one year, in two years, any time. Then you got married and he was quiet for many months. But he started talking again. He said you were the only American from our village. I asked him once what was so great about being the only American from our village. He said it was an honour.

'Some of us used to go for walks. He talked all the time. And he talked only of you. We got fed up with his talk, to tell you the truth. We had a foot in the grave, all of us. What did we care for your achievements; what you did and what you did not do. I told him so one day. He was angry with me. I suppose I should not have said that. He stopped coming with us. He did not go for walks for a while, then he started to go by himself. He chose different timings and took a different route. But I would see him now and then. He had a stoop. You are developing a stoop similar to his, if you don't mind my saying so.'

The *ashtamp farosh* paused. He seemed to have lost the thread of his thoughts. Then he started again. 'After his retirement he had a shave every other day. We used to go together, to the same barber. He would have his shave first because he did not like to wait. But he had to wait anyway while I had *my* shave. It came to the same thing. But he did not mind that. Some people are strange.

'Then, all at once, he started to shave every day. He also had two shirts made. Two new shirts and a suit. He said it was too costly to have a shave every day in the bazaar, so he bought his own razor. A razor and a cake of soap. I asked him what on earth had got into him? Why in God's name did he *have* to shave every day. He took me aside and said he was expecting a ticket. What ticket? I asked him. He said he was expecting a ticket from you to visit America. A return ticket. He looked at me when he said that his eyes twinkled.'

The *ashtamp farosh* fidgeted inside his pockets for several moments and pulled out a bidi. He did not light it.

'To tell you the truth I was impressed. Kundan Lal going to America, that was not something you could laugh away. I told some fellows about the ticket and before morning the whole village knew about it.

'You see what I mean? Maybe you don't. Maybe you don't have villages like ours in America but you must try to understand what it meant after the whole village knew you were going to send him a ticket. Did you send him a ticket?'

The question took Dr Khanna by surprise. He looked confused. He said: 'I could not, I did not . . .'

'I thought as much,' said the *ashtamp farosh*, cutting him short. 'Then he did another foolish thing: he turned religious. All his life I had never seen him inside a temple and now he went there every evening. Morning and evening. And that wasn't all. He started even to sing, the old fool. What did he know about singing? Yet he would stand with all those old women and sing, like a donkey, if you don't mind my saying so. I say this only because it hurt me to see him making a fool of himself. I caught hold of him in the street one day and I told him what I thought of him. What do you expect from God, I asked him. Your son? A letter from your son? A ticket? What? Why was he cutting himself off from the rest of us, I asked him. If you were doing well, as he said, what was eating him. Why was he cutting himself off from his friends? I thought he would be angry. But he wasn't. He just stood there in the middle of the street and looked at me, looked right through me as though I were air. Then he went off muttering to himself. I saw him many times after that but I did not speak to him again. I did not want trouble, to tell you the truth. Then he fell ill.'

The *ashtamp farosh* lit his bidi, took a deep pull and, on an impulse, threw it away. Dr Khanna could see it smouldering in the verandah. The smoke nauseated him. Outside, it was totally dark. The winter night had set in. 'Why did you not send him the ticket?' the *ashtamp farosh* asked suddenly. Once again Dr Khanna was taken by surprise. 'I could not,' he said. 'I did not have the money.'

The *ashtamp farosh* looked at him, puzzled, but he said nothing. 'Nor did your father have the money. So he stayed home and became quiet once again.'

The *ashtamp farosh* fell silent. His expressions became vague. He let his hands drop into his pockets where they fidgeted with a variety of objects.

'Of course he had never had much money. He had a scholarship in school that paid for his fees. But he had only two pyjamas and two kurtas and he had no shoes. We went to school together and came back together. Between the school and our village is the *cho*. Do you remember the *cho*? It runs in the rains. Nine months it is dry. In summer the sand gets very hot. Have you seen how they roast corn in hot sand. You could roast corn in the *cho*. It was half a mile of boiling sand in May that we had to cross. No more, no less. And your father had no shoes. So he would stop this end of the *cho* and take a handful of *dhak* leaves and tie them on his naked feet with a string and he would cross the sand. And if the string came off he would jump around screaming on one foot while I tied the leaves back on to his foot. That is how your father crossed the *cho* for ten years, Dr Khanna,' said the *ashtamp farosh*.

His tone was not harsh. He was not even looking at him but somehow Dr Khanna had the unreasonable feeling that the old man was going to slap him. He wanted to get away and he looked helplessly at the Principal but the *ashtamp farosh* stood between them and the doorway. He had begun to talk again, in a softer voice, as though to himself. 'I told him not to do it. I told him he was being stupid.'

After another silence he addressed them again, 'When he fell ill your sister came. He asked me to write to you. I sent you a telegram. It cost me one hundred rupees but you chose to reply only by a letter. I did not understand what you said except that you had to attend some conference. I told your father you had a conference. "Does he say when he can come?" he asked. I told him you had not said when you could come. "He must be busy," he said. He did not mention you again. He got better. One day he said, "Radhey, let us go and look at our old desk." It was the month of May and it was very hot but he was feeling better and I thought a trip to town will do him good. We went in a rickshaw. And the desk was where it had always been. The same room, the same row, the same place. There were his initials on his side and mine on mine. We went to the Honours Board and had a look at his name. We started back and came to the *cho*. Then the mad thought entered his head. It was madness. No more, no less. There are no words to describe such madness. He even looked mad to me. He stopped the rickshaw before the *cho*. He got off and kicked away his shoes and started plucking at the leaves of *dhak*. He could not tie them because he had arthritis and he could not bend. "Tie these on my feet, Radhey," he ordered me. "You are mad, Kundan Lal," I told him, but he had a bad look on his face and I knew it was no use arguing with him. I thought he would come to his senses when he touched the boiling sand. But I told you he wasn't himself. He stepped into the *cho*. I followed him carrying his shoes hoping he would stop, shouting at him to stop. I could feel the sand through my soles but told you he had lost his head. He walked the whole half mile. The leaves fell off on the way. God himself could not have stopped him. He had fever by the time he got home. The next day he died.'

Dr Khanna winced but his training in the new civilization had been perfect.

'I was very sorry to hear of his death,' he said calmly.

'We must go now, Radhey Mohanji,' said the Principal. He stretched his hand but the *ashtamp farosh* was gone, shuffling through the dark, a bidi in his mouth.

That weekend Dr Khanna and family boarded a plane for Chicago. At Chicago they changed. As the plane for Madison got aloft Mrs Joanne Khanna was heard to say to her husband, 'What's the matter, darling, you keep staring at your feet. I have been watching you for the last two days and you've done nothing but stare at your feet.'

Since then a lot of people have been heard to say that. To a psychiatrist Dr Khanna has confided that he has periods of great burning in his feet. He has further indicated that he thinks he has been cursed. Dr Khanna's output of research since he came back has been zero. He has generally come to be known as the man who does nothing but stare at his feet.

I Am Not That Woman

Kishwar Naheed
Translated by Mahmood Jamal

Kishwar Naheed is a leading contemporary poet from Pakistan; she
writes in Urdu.

I am not that woman
selling you socks and shoes!
Remember me, I am the one you hid
in your walls of stone, while you roamed
free as the breeze, not knowing
that my voice cannot be smothered by stones.

I am the one you crushed
with the weight of custom and tradition
not knowing
that light cannot be hidden in darkness.
Remember me,
I am the one in whose lap
you picked flowers
and planted thorns and embers
not knowing
that chains cannot smother my fragrance.

I am the woman
whom you bought and sold
in the name of my own chastity
not knowing
that I can walk on water
when I am drowning.

I am the one you married off
to get rid of a burden
not knowing
that a nation of captive minds
cannot be free.

I am the commodity you traded in,
my chastity, my motherhood, my loyalty.
Now it is time for me to flower free.
The woman on that poster,
half-naked, selling socks and shoes—
No, no, I am not that woman!

The Twelfth Man

Iftikhar Arif
Translated by Mahmood Jamal

Iftikhar Arif is a contemporary poet who writes in Urdu and lives in London.

In fine weather
numerous spectators come
to applaud their team
and raise their idols' esteem.
I, separate and alone,
salute the twelfth man.

What a strange player
is the twelfth man!
The game goes on,
the applause goes on,
the crowd roars
and he, alien to it all,
waits, waits
for that moment,
for that instant
when disaster strikes.
When he comes out to play,
to the sound of clapping,
some word of praise,
some shout of applause
may be raised in his name;
and he, too, becomes
respected like the rest.

But this happens seldom.
Yet it's said that
a player's relationship
with the game
is lifelong;
though this relationship
can also break,
the heart that sinks
with the last whistle
can also break.

You are a twelfth man,
Iftikhar:
You too wait
for that moment
when disaster strikes,
some calamity.
You too, Iftikhar Arif,
you too will sink,
you too will break.

A Prison Nightfall

Faiz Ahmad Faiz
Translated by Mahmood Jamal

This poem is translated from Urdu. Faiz, who died in 1984, was widely
regarded as the leading Urdu poet of his generation.

> The night descends
> step by silent step
> down the stairway of stars.
> The breeze goes by me
> like a kindly whispered phrase.
>
> The homeless trees of the prison yard
> are absorbed, making patterns
> against the sky.
>
> On the roof's high crest
> the loving hand of moonlight rests.
> The starry river is drowned in dust
> and the sky glows silver with moonlight.
> In the dark foliage
> shadows play with the wind
> as a wave of painful loss
> invades the heart.
>
> Defiantly, a thought tells me
> how sweet life is at this instant:
> Those who brew the poison of cruelty
> will not win, tomorrow or today.
> They can put out the lamps
> where lovers meet;
> they cannot blind the moon!

A Horse and Two Goats

R. K. Narayan

This short story by one of India's leading English-language novelists is set in south India and recounts a succession of misunderstandings between an impoverished villager and an American tourist.

Of the seven hundred thousand villages dotting the map of India, in which the majority of India's five hundred million live, flourish, and die, Kritam was probably the tiniest, indicated on the district survey map by a microscopic dot, the map being meant more for the revenue official out to collect tax than for the guidance of the motorist, who in any case could not hope to reach it since it sprawled far from the highway at the end of a rough track furrowed up by the iron-hooped wheels of bullock carts. But its size did not prevent its giving itself the grandiose name Kritam, which meant in Tamil 'coronet' or 'crown' on the brow of this subcontinent. The village consisted of less than thirty houses, only one of them built with brick and cement. Painted a brilliant yellow and blue all over with gorgeous carvings of gods and gargoyles on its balustrade, it was known as the Big House. The other houses, distributed in four streets, were generally of bamboo thatch, straw, mud, and other unspecified material. Muni's was the last house in the fourth street, beyond which stretched the fields. In his prosperous days Muni had owned a flock of forty sheep and goats and sallied forth every morning driving the flock to the highway a couple of miles away. There he would sit on the pedestal of a clay statue of a horse while his cattle grazed around. He carried a crook at the end of a bamboo pole and snapped foliage from the avenue trees to feed his flock; he also gathered faggots and dry sticks, bundled them, and carried them home for fuel at sunset.

113

His wife lit the domestic fire at dawn, boiled water in a mud pot, threw into it a handful of millet flour, added salt, and gave him his first nourishment for the day. When he started out, she would put in his hand a packed lunch, once again the same millet cooked into a little ball, which he could swallow with a raw onion at midday. She was old, but he was older and needed all the attention she could give him in order to be kept alive.

His fortunes had declined gradually, unnoticed. From a flock of forty which he drove into a pen at night, his stock had now come down to two goats, which were not worth the rent of a half rupee a month the Big House charged for the use of the pen in their back yard. And so the two goats were tethered to the trunk of a drumstick tree which grew in front of his hut and from which occasionally Muni could shake down drumsticks. This morning he got six. He carried them in with a sense of triumph. Although no one could say precisely who owned the tree, it was his because he lived in its shadow.

She said, 'If you were content with the drumstick leaves alone, I could boil and salt some for you.'

'Oh, I am tired of eating those leaves. I have a craving to chew the drumstick out of sauce, I tell you.'

'You have only four teeth in your jaw, but your craving is for big things. All right, get the stuff for the sauce, and I will prepare it for you. After all, next year you may not be alive to ask for anything. But first get me all the stuff, including a measure of rice or millet, and I will satisfy your unholy craving. Our store is empty today. Dhall, chili, curry leaves, mustard, coriander, gingelley oil, and one large potato. Go out and get all this.' He repeated the list after her in order not to miss any item and walked off to the shop in the third street.

He sat on an upturned packing case below the platform of the shop. The shopman paid no attention to him. Muni kept clearing his throat, coughing, and sneezing until the shopman could not stand it any more and demanded, 'What ails you? You will fly off that seat into the gutter if you sneeze so hard, young man.' Muni laughed inordinately, in order to please the shopman, at being called 'young man'. The shopman softened and said, 'You have enough of the imp inside to keep a second wife busy, but for the fact the old lady is still alive.' Muni laughed appropriately again at this joke. It completely won the shopman over; he liked his sense of humour to be appreciated. Muni engaged his attention in local gossip for a few minutes, which always ended with a reference to the postman's wife who had eloped to the city some months before.

The shopman felt most pleased to hear the worst of the postman, who had cheated him. Being an itinerant postman, he returned home to Kritam only once in ten days and every time managed to slip away again without passing the shop in the third street. By thus humouring the shopman, Muni could always ask for one or two items of food, promising repayment later. Some days the shopman was in a good mood and gave in, and sometimes he would lose his temper suddenly and bark at Muni for daring to ask for credit.

This was such a day, and Muni could not progress beyond two items listed as essential components. The shopman was also displaying a remarkable memory for old facts and figures and took out an oblong ledger to support his observations. Muni felt impelled to rise and flee. But his self-respect kept him in his seat and made him listen to the worst things about himself. The shopman concluded, 'If you could find five rupees and a quarter, you will have paid off an ancient debt and then could apply for admission to swarga. How much have you got now?'

'I will pay you everything on the first of the next month.'

'As always, and whom do you expect to rob by then?'

Muni felt caught and mumbled, 'My daughter has sent word that she will be sending me money.'

'Have you a daughter?' sneered the shopman. 'And she is sending you money! For what purpose, may I know?'

'Birthday, fiftieth birthday,' said Muni quietly.

'Birthday! How old are you?'

Muni repeated weakly, not being sure of it himself, 'Fifty.' He always calculated his age from the time of the great famine when he stood as high as the parapet around the village well, but who could calculate such things accurately nowadays with so many famines occurring? The shopman felt encouraged when other customers stood around to watch and comment. Muni thought helplessly, 'My poverty is exposed to everybody. But what can I do?'

'More likely you are seventy,' said the shopman. 'You also forget that you mentioned a birthday five weeks ago when you wanted castor oil for your holy bath.'

'Bath! Who can dream of a bath when you have to scratch the tank-bed for a bowl of water? We would all be parched and dead but for the Big House, where they let us take a pot of water from their well.' After saying this Muni unobtrusively rose and moved off.

He told his wife, 'That scoundrel would not give me anything. So go out and sell the drumsticks for what they are worth.'

He flung himself down in a corner to recoup from the fatigue of his visit to the shop. His wife said, 'You are getting no sauce today, nor anything else. I can't find anything to give you to eat. Fast till the evening, it'll do you good. Take the goats and be gone now,' she cried and added, 'Don't come back before the sun is down.' He knew that if he obeyed her she would somehow conjure up some food for him in the evening. Only he must be careful not to argue and irritate her. Her temper was undependable in the morning but improved by evening time. She was sure to go out and work—grind corn in the Big House, sweep or scrub somewhere, and earn enough to buy foodstuff and keep a dinner ready for him in the evening.

Unleashing the goats from the drumstick tree, Muni stared out, driving them ahead and uttering weird cries from time to time in order to urge them on. He passed through the village with his head bowed in thought. He did not want to look at anyone or be accosted. A couple of cronies lounging in the temple corridor hailed him, but he ignored their call. They had known him in the days of affluence when he lorded over a flock of fleecy sheep, not the miserable gawky goats that he had today. Of course he also used to have a few goats for those who fancied them, but real wealth lay in sheep; they bred fast and people came and bought the fleece in the shearing season; and then that famous butcher from the town came over on the weekly market days bringing him betel leaves, tobacco, and often enough some bhang, which they smoked in a hut in the coconut grove, undisturbed by wives and well-wishers. After a smoke one felt light and elated and inclined to forgive everyone including that brother-in-law of his who had once tried to set fire to his home. But all this seemed like the memories of a previous birth. Some pestilence afflicted his cattle (he could of course guess who had laid his animals under a curse), and even the friendly butcher would not touch one at half the price . . . and now here he was left with the two scraggy creatures. He wished someone would rid him of their company too. The shopman had said that he was seventy. At seventy, one only waited to be summoned by God. When he was dead what would his wife do? They had lived in each other's company since they were children. He was told on their day of wedding that he was ten years old and she was eight. During the wedding ceremony they had had to recite their respective ages and names. He had thrashed her only a few times in their career, and later she had had the upper hand. Progeny, none. Perhaps a large progeny would have brought him the blessing of the gods. Fertility brought merit. People with fourteen sons were always so prosperous and at peace with the world and themselves. He recollected the thrill he had felt when he mentioned a daughter to that shopman; although it was not believed, what if he did not have a daughter?—his cousin in the next village had many daughters, and any one of them was as good as his; he was fond of them all and would buy them sweets if he could afford it. Still, everyone in the village whispered behind their backs that Muni and his wife were a barren couple. He avoided looking at anyone; they all professed to be so high up, and everyone else in the village had more money than he. 'I am the poorest fellow in our caste and no wonder that they spurn me, but I won't look at them either,' and so he passed on with his eyes downcast along the edge of the street, and people left him also very much alone, commenting only to the extent, 'Ah, there he goes with his two goats; if he slits their throats, he may have more peace of mind.' 'What has he to worry about anyway? They live on nothing and have none to worry about.' Thus people commented when he passed through the village. Only on the outskirts did he lift his head and look up. He urged and bullied the goats until they meandered along to the foot of the horse statue on the edge of the village. He sat on its pedestal for the rest of the day. The advantage of this was that he could watch the highway and see the lorries and buses pass through to the hills, and it gave him a sense of belonging to a larger world. The pedestal of the statue was broad enough for him to move around as the sun travelled up and westward; or he could also crouch under the belly of the horse, for shade.

The horse was nearly life-size, moulded out of clay, baked, burnt, and brightly coloured, and reared its head proudly, prancing its forelegs in the air and flourishing its tail in a loop; beside the horse stood a warrior with scythe-like mustachios, bulging eyes, and aquiline nose. The old image-makers believed in indicating a man of strength by bulging out his eyes and sharpening his moustache tips, and also decorated the man's chest with beads which looked today like blobs of mud through the ravages of sun and wind and rain (when it came), but Muni would insist that he had known the beads to sparkle like the nine gems at one time in his life. The horse itself was said to have been as white as a dhobi-washed sheet, and had had on its back a cover of pure brocade of red and black lace, matching the multicoloured sash around the waist of the warrior. But none in the village remembered the splendour as no one noticed its existence. Even Muni, who spent all his waking hours at its foot; never bothered to look up. It was untouched even by the young vandals of the village who gashed tree trunks with knives and tried to topple off milestones and inscribed lewd designs on all walls. This statue had been closer to the population of the village at one time, when this spot bordered the village; but when the highway was laid through (or perhaps when the tank and wells dried up completely here) the village moved a couple of miles inland.

Muni sat at the foot of the statue, watching his two goats graze in the arid soil among the cactus and lantana bushes. He looked at the sun; it had tilted westward no doubt, but it was not the time yet to go back home; if he went too early his wife would have no food for him. Also he must give her time to cool off her temper and feel sympathetic, and then she would scrounge and manage to get some food. He watched the mountain road for a time signal. When the green bus appeared around the bend he could leave, and his wife would feel pleased that he had let the goats feed long enough.

He noticed now a new sort of vehicle coming down at full speed. It looked like both a motor car and a bus. He used to be intrigued by the novelty of such spectacles, but of late work was going on at the source of the river on the mountain and an assortment of people and traffic went past him, and he took it all casually and described to his wife, later in the day, everything he saw. Today, while he observed the yellow vehicle coming down, he was wondering how to describe it later to his wife when it sputtered and stopped in front of him. A red-faced foreigner, who had been driving it, got down and went round it, stooping, looking, and poking under the vehicle; then he straightened himself up, looked at the dashboard, stared in Muni's direction, and approached him. 'Excuse me, is there a gas station nearby, or do I have to wait until another car comes—' He suddenly looked up at the clay horse and cried, 'Marvellous,' without completing his sentence. Muni felt he should get up and run away, and cursed his age. He could not readily put his limbs into action; some years ago he could outrun a cheetah, as happened once when he went to the forest to cut fuel and it was then that two of his sheep were mauled—a sign that bad times were coming. Though he tried, he could not easily extricate himself from his seat, and then there was also the problem of the goats. He could not leave them behind.

The red-faced man wore khaki clothes—evidently a police-man or a soldier. Muni said to himself, 'He will chase or shoot if I start running. Some dogs chase only those who run—oh, Shiva protect me. I don't know why this man should be after me.' Meanwhile the foreigner cried, 'Marvellous!' again, nodding his head. He paced around the statue with his eyes fixed on it. Muni sat frozen for a while, and then fidgeted and tried to edge away. Now the other man suddenly pressed his palms together in a salute, smiled, and said, 'Namaste! How do you do?'

At which Muni spoke the only English expressions he had learnt, 'Yes, no.' Having exhausted his English vocabulary, he started in Tamil: 'My name is Muni. These two goats are mine, and no one can gainsay it—though our village is full of slanderers these days who will not hesitate to say that what belongs to a man doesn't belong to him.' He rolled his eyes and shuddered at the thought of evil-minded men and women peopling his village.

The foreigner faithfully looked in the direction indicated by Muni's fingers, gazed for a while at the two goats and the rocks, and with a puzzled expression took out his silver cigarette case and lit a cigarette. Suddenly remembering the courtesies of the season, he asked, 'Do you smoke?' Muni answered, 'Yes, no.' Whereupon the red-faced man took a cigarette and gave it to Muni, who received it with surprise, having had no offer of a smoke from anyone for years now. Those days when he smoked bhang were gone with his sheep and the large-hearted butcher. Nowadays he was not able to find even matches, let alone bhang. (His wife went across and borrowed a fire at dawn from a neighbour.) He had always wanted to smoke a cigarette; only once did the shopman give him one on credit, and he remembered how good it had tasted. The other flicked the lighter open and offered a light to Muni. Muni felt so confused about how to act that he blew on it and put it out. The other, puzzled but undaunted, flourished his lighter, presented it again, and lit Muni's cigarette. Muni drew a deep puff and started coughing; it was racking, no doubt, but extremely pleasant. When his cough subsided he wiped his eyes and took stock of the situation, understanding that the other man was not an Inquisitor of any kind. Yet, in order to make sure, he remained wary. No need to run away from a man who gave him such a potent smoke. His head was reeling from the effect of one of those strong American cigarettes made with roasted tobacco.

The man said, 'I come from New York,' took out a wallet from his hip pocket, and presented his card.

Muni shrank away from the card. Perhaps he was trying to present a warrant and arrest him. Beware of khaki, one part of his mind warned. Take all the cigarettes or bhang or whatever is offered, but don't get caught. Beware of khaki. He wished he weren't seventy as the shopman had said. At seventy one didn't run, but surrendered to whatever came. He could only ward off trouble by talk. So he went on, all in the chaste Tamil for which Kritam was famous. (Even the worst detractors could not deny that the famous poetess Avvaiyar was born in this area, although no one could say whether it was in Kritam or Kuppam, the adjoining village.) Out of this heritage the Tamil language gushed through Muni in an unimpeded flow. He said, 'Before God, sir, Bhagwan, who sees everything, I tell you, sir, that we know nothing of the case. If the murder was committed, whoever did it will not escape. Bhagwan is all-seeing. Don't ask me about it. I know nothing.' A body had been found mutilated and thrown under a tamarind tree at the border between Kritam and Kuppam a few weeks before, giving rise to much gossip and speculation. Muni added an explanation. 'Anything is possible there. People over there will stop at nothing.' The foreigner nodded his head and listened courteously though he understood nothing.

'I am sure you know when this horse was made,' said the red man and smiled ingratiatingly.

Muni reacted to the relaxed atmosphere by smiling himself, and pleaded, 'Please go away, sir, I know nothing. I promise we will hold him for you if we see any bad character around, and we will bury him up to his neck in a coconut pit if he tries to escape; but our village has always had a clean record. Must definitely be the other village.'

Now the red man implored, 'Please, please, I will speak slowly, please try to understand me. Can't you understand even a simple word of English? Everyone in this country seems to know English. I have gotten along with English everywhere in this country, but you don't speak it. Have you any religious or spiritual scruples against English speech?'

Muni made some indistinct sounds in his throat and shook his head. Encouraged, the other went on to explain at length, uttering each syllable with care and deliberation. Presently he sidled over and took a seat beside the old man, explaining, 'You see, last August, we probably had the hottest summer in history, and I was working in shirt-sleeves in my office on the fortieth floor of the Empire State Building. We had a power failure one day, you know, and there I was stuck for four hours, no elevator, no air conditioning. All the way in the train I kept thinking, and the minute I reached home in Connecticut, I told my wife Ruth, "We will visit India this winter, it's time to look at other civilizations." Next day she called the travel agent first thing and told him to fix it, and so here I am. Ruth came with me but is staying back at Srinager, and I am the one doing the rounds and joining her later.'

Muni looked reflective at the end of this long oration and said, rather feebly, 'Yes, no,' as a concession to the other's language, and went on in Tamil, 'When I was this high'—he indicated a foot high—'I had heard my uncle say . . .'

No one can tell what he was planning to say, as the other interrupted him at this stage to ask, 'Boy, what is the secret of your teeth? How old are you?'

The old man forgot what he had started to say and remarked, 'Sometimes we too lose our cattle. Jackals or cheetahs may sometimes carry them off, but sometimes it is just theft from over in the next village, and then we will know who has done it. Our priest at the temple can see in the camphor flame the face of the thief, and when he is caught . . .' He gestured with his hands a perfect mincing of meat.

The American watched his hands intently and said, 'I know what you mean. Chop something? Maybe I am holding you up and you want to chop wood? Where is your axe? Hand it to me and show me what to chop. I do enjoy it, you know, just a hobby. We get a lot of driftwood along the backwater near my house, and on Sundays I do nothing but chop wood for the fireplace. I really feel different when I watch the fire in the fireplace, although it may take all the sections of the Sunday *New York Times* to get a fire started.' And he smiled at this reference.

Muni felt totally confused but decided the best thing would be to make an attempt to get away from this place. He tried to edge out, saying, 'Must go home,' and turned to go. The other seized his shoulder and said desperately, 'Is there no one, absolutely no one here, to translate for me?' He looked up and down the road, which was deserted in this hot afternoon; a sudden gust of wind churned up the dust and dead leaves on the roadside into a ghostly column and propelled it towards the mountain road. The stranger almost pinioned Muni's back to the statue and asked, 'Isn't this statue yours? Why don't you sell it to me?'

The old man now understood the reference to the horse, thought for a second, and said in his own language, 'I was an urchin this high when I heard my grandfather explain this horse and warrior, and my grandfather himself was this high when he heard his grandfather, whose grandfather . . .'

The other man interrupted him. 'I don't want to seem to have stopped here for nothing. I will offer you a good price for this,' he said, indicating the horse. He had concluded without the least doubt that Muni owned this mud horse. Perhaps he guessed by the way he sat on its pedestal, like other souvenir sellers in this country presiding over their wares.

Muni followed the man's eyes and pointing fingers and dimly understood the subject matter and, feeling relieved that the theme of the mutilated body had been abandoned at least for the time being, said again, enthusiastically, 'I was this high when my grandfather told me about this horse and the warrior, and my grandfather was this high when he himself . . .' and he was getting into a deeper bog of reminiscence each time he tried to indicate the antiquity of the statue.

The Tamil that Muni spoke was stimulating even as pure sound, and the foreigner listened with fascination. 'I wish I had my tape-recorder here,' he said, assuming the pleasantest expression. 'Your language sounds wonderful. I get a kick out of every word you utter, here'—he indicated his ears—'but you don't have to waste your breath in sales talk. I appreciate the article. You don't have to explain its points.'

'I never went to a school, in those days only Brahmin went to schools, but we had to go out and work in the fields morning till night, from sowing to harvest time . . . and when Pongal came and we had cut the harvest, my father allowed me to go out and play with others at the tank, and so I don't know the Parangi language you speak, even little fellows in your country probably speak the Parangi language, but here only learned men and officers know it. We had a postman in our village who could speak to you boldly in your language, but his wife ran away with someone and he does not speak to anyone at all nowadays. Who would if a wife did what she did? Women must be watched; otherwise they will sell themselves and the home.' And he laughed at his own quip.

The foreigner laughed heartily, took out another cigarette, and offered it to Muni, who now smoked with ease, deciding to stay on if the fellow was going to be so good as to keep up his cigarette supply. The American now stood up on the pedestal in the attitude of a demonstrative lecturer and said, running his finger along some of the carved decorations around the horse's neck, speaking slowly and uttering his words syllable by syllable, 'I could give a sales talk for this better than anyone else . . . This is a marvellous combination of yellow and indigo, though faded now . . . How do you people of this country achieve these flaming colours?'

Muni, now assured that the subject was still the horse and not the dead body, said, 'This is our guardian, it means death to our adversaries. At the end of Kali Yuga, this world and all other worlds will be destroyed, and the Redeemer will come in the shape of a horse called "Kalki", this horse will come to life and gallop and trample down all bad men.' As he spoke of bad men the figures of his shopman and his brother-in-law assumed concrete forms in his mind, and he revelled for a moment in the predicament of the fellow under the horse's hoof: served him right for trying to set fire to his home . . .

While he was brooding on this pleasant vision, the foreigner utilized the pause to say, 'I assure you that this will have the best home in the USA. I'll push away the bookcase, you know I love books and am a member of five book clubs, and the choice and bonus volumes mount up to a pile really in our living room, as high as this horse itself. But they'll have to go. Ruth may disapprove, but I will convince her. The TV may have to be shifted too. We can't have everything in the living room. Ruth will probably say what about when we have a party? I'm going to keep him right in the middle of the room. I don't see how that can interfere with the party—we'll stand around him and have our drinks.'

Muni continued his description of the end of the world. 'Our pundit discoursed at the temple once how the oceans are going to close over the earth in a huge wave and swallow us—this horse will grow bigger than the biggest wave and carry on its back only the good people and kick into the floods the evil ones—plenty of them about—' he said reflectively. 'Do you know when it is going to happen?' he asked.

The foreigner now understood by the tone of the other that a question was being asked and said, 'How am I transporting it? I can push the seat back and make room in the rear. That van can take in an elephant'—waving precisely at the back of the seat.

Muni was still hovering on visions of avatars and said again, 'I never missed our pundit's discourses at the temple in those days during every bright half of the month, although he'd go on all night, and he told us that Vishnu is the highest god. Whenever evil men trouble us, he comes down to save us. He has come many times. The first time he incarnated as a great fish, and lifted the scriptures on his back when the floods and sea waves . . .'

'I am not a millionaire, but a modest businessman. My trade is coffee.'

Amidst all this wilderness of obscure sound Muni caught the word 'coffee' and said, 'If you want to drink "kapi", drive further up, in the next town, they have Friday market, and there they open "kapi-otels"—so I learn from passers-by. Don't think I wander about. I go nowhere and look for nothing.' His thoughts went back to the avatars. 'The first avatar was in the shape of a

125

little fish in a bowl of water, but every hour it grew bigger and bigger and became in the end a huge whale which the seas could not contain, and on the back of the whale the holy books were supported, saved and carried.' Once he had launched on the first avatar, it was inevitable that he should go on to the next, a wild boar on whose tusk the earth was lifted when a vicious conqueror of the earth carried it off and hid it at the bottom of the sea. After describing this avatar Muni concluded, 'God will always save us whenever we are troubled by evil beings. When we were young we staged at full moon the story of the avatars. That's how I know the stories; we played them all night until the sun rose, and sometimes the European collector would come to watch, bringing his own chair. I had a good voice and so they always taught me songs and gave me the women's roles. I was always Goddess Lakshmi, and they dressed me in a brocade sari, loaned from the Big House . . .'

The foreigner said, 'I repeat I am not a millionaire. Ours is a modest business; after all, we can't afford to buy more than sixty minutes of TV time in a month, which works out to two minutes a day, that's all, although in the course of time we'll maybe sponsor a one-hour show regularly if our sales graph continues to go up . . .'

Muni was intoxicated by the memory of his theatrical days and was about to explain how he had painted his face and worn a wig and diamond earrings when the visitor, feeling that he had spent too much time already, said, 'Tell me, will you accept a hundred rupees or not for the horse? I'd love to take the whiskered soldier also but no space for him this year. I'll have to cancel my air ticket and take a boat home, I suppose. Ruth can go by air if she likes, but I will go with the horse and keep him in my cabin all the way if necessary.' And he smiled at the picture of himself voyaging across the seas hugging this horse. He added, 'I will have to pad it with straw so that it doesn't break . . .'

'When we played *Ramayana*, they dressed me as Sita,' added Muni. 'A teacher came and taught us the songs for the drama and we gave him fifty rupees. He incarnated himself as Rama, and He alone could destroy Ravana, the demon with ten heads who shook all the worlds; do you know the story of *Ramayana?*'

'I have my station wagon as you see. I can push the seat back and take the horse in if you will just lend me a hand with it.'

'Do you know *Mahabharata?* Krishna was the eighth avatar of Vishnu, incarnated to help the Five Brothers regain their kingdom. When Krishna was a baby he danced on the thousand-hooded giant serpent and trampled it to death; and then he suckled the breasts of the demoness and left them flat as a disc though when she came to him her bosoms were large, like mounds of earth on the banks of a dug up canal.' He indicated two mounds with his hands. The stranger was completely mystified by the gesture. For the first time he said, 'I really wonder what you are saying because your answer is crucial. We have come to the point when we should be ready to talk business.'

'When the tenth avatar comes, do you know where you and I will be?' asked the old man.

'Lend me a hand and I can lift off the horse from its pedestal after picking out the cement at the joints. We can do anything if we have a basis of understanding.'

At this stage the mutual mystification was complete, and there was no need even to carry on a guessing game at the meaning of words. The old man chattered away in a spirit of balancing off the credits and debits of conversational exchange, and said in order to be on the credit side, 'Oh, honourable one, I hope God has blessed you with numerous progeny. I say this because you seem to be a good man, willing to stay beside an old man and talk to him, while all day I have none to talk to except when somebody stops by to ask for a piece of tobacco. But I seldom have it, tobacco is not what it used to be at one time, and I have given up chewing. I cannot afford it nowadays.' Noting the other's interest in his speech, Muni felt encouraged to ask, 'How many children have you?' with appropriate gestures with his hands. Realizing that a question was being asked, the red man replied, 'I said a hundred,' which encouraged Muni to go into details. 'How many of your children are boys and how many girls? Where are they? Is your daughter married? Is it difficult to find a son-in-law in your country also?'

In answer to these questions the red man dashed his hand into his pocket and brought forth his wallet in order to take immediate advantage of the bearish trend in the market. He flourished a hundred-rupee currency note and said, 'Well, this is what I meant.'

The old man now realized that some financial element was entering their talk. He peered closely at the currency note, the like of which he had never seen in his life; he knew the five and ten by their colours although always in other people's hands, while his own earning at any time was in coppers and nickels. What was this man flourishing the note for? Perhaps asking for change. He laughed to himself at the notion of anyone coming to him for changing a thousand- or ten-thousand-rupee note. He said with a grin, 'Ask our village headman, who is also a moneylender; he can change even a lakh of rupees in gold sovereigns if you prefer it that way; he thinks nobody knows, but dig the floor of his puja room and your head will reel at the sight of the hoard. The man disguises himself in rags just to mislead the public. Talk to the headman yourself because he goes mad at the sight of me. Someone took away his pumpkins with the creeper and he, for some reason, thinks it was me and my goats . . . that's why I never let my goats be seen anywhere near the farms.' His eyes travelled to his goats nosing about, attempting to wrest nutrition from minute greenery peeping out of rock and dry earth.

The foreigner followed his look and decided that it would be a sound policy to show an interest in the old man's pets. He went up casually to them and stroked their backs with every show of courteous attention. Now the truth dawned on the old man. His dream of a lifetime was about to be realized. He understood that the red man was actually making an offer for the goats. He had reared them up in the hope of selling them some day and, with the capital, opening a small shop on this very spot. Sitting here, watching towards the hills, he had often dreamt how he would put up a thatched roof here, spread a gunny sack out on the ground, and display on it fried nuts, coloured sweets, and green coconut for the thirsty and famished wayfarers on the highway, which was sometimes very busy. The animals were not prize ones for a cattle show, but he had spent his occasional savings to provide them some fancy diet now and then, and they did not look too bad. While he was reflecting thus, the red man shook his hand and left on his palm one hundred rupees in tens now, suddenly realizing that this was what the old man was asking. 'It is all for you or you may share it if you have a partner.'

The old man pointed at the station wagon and asked, 'Are you carrying them off in that?'

'Yes, of course,' said the other, understanding the transportation part of it.

The old man said, 'This will be their first ride in a motor car. Carry them off after I get out of sight, otherwise they will never follow you, but only me even if I am travelling on the path to Yama Loka.' He laughed at his own joke, brought his palms together in a salute, turned round and went off, and was soon out of sight beyond a clump of thicket.

The red man looked at the goats grazing peacefully. Perched on the pedestal of the horse, as the westerly sun touched off the ancient faded colours of the statue with a fresh splendour, he ruminated, 'He must be gone to fetch some help, I suppose!' and settled down to wait. When a truck came downhill, he stopped it and got the help of a couple of men to detach the horse from its pedestal and place it in his station wagon. He gave them five rupees each, and for a further payment they siphoned off gas from the truck, and helped him to start his engine.

Muni hurried homeward with the cash securely tucked away at his waist in his dhoti. He shut the street door and stole up softly to his wife as she squatted before the lit oven wondering if by a miracle food would drop from the sky. Muni displayed his fortune for the day. She snatched the notes from him, counted them by the glow of the fire, and cried, 'One hundred rupees! How did you come by it? Have you been stealing?'

'I have sold our goats to a red-faced man. He was absolutely crazy to have them, gave me all this money and carried them off in his motor car!'

Hardly had these words left his lips when they heard bleating outside. She opened the door and saw the two goats at her door. 'Here they are!' she said. 'What's the meaning of all this?'

He muttered a great curse and seized one of the goats by its ears and shouted, 'Where is that man? Don't you know you are his? Why did you come back?' The goat only wriggled in his grip. He asked the same question of the other too. The goat shook itself off. His wife glared at him and declared, 'If you have thieved, the police will come tonight and break your bones. Don't involve me. I will go away to my parents . . .'

Rough Passage

R. Parthasarathy

These three sections are from a sequence of that title, written in English. The sequence opens in London in the Sixties, and then describes the journey back to India and reunion with the poet's family. This is the 'rough passage' of the title. The second poem printed here describes stopping at Goa, the former Portuguese colony on the west coast of India, near Bombay. The line 'he stands alone' refers to Camoens, a Portuguese poet who wrote an epic poem celebrating the achievements of the Portuguese navigator Vasco da Gama, who established the first Portuguese settlements in India. Tamil, the language referred to in the third section, is Parthasarathy's mother-tongue.

1

Through holes in a wall, as it were,
lamps burned in the fog.
In a basement flat, conversation

filled the night, while Ravi Shankar,
cigarette stubs, empty bottles of stout
and crisps provided the necessary pauses.

He had spent his youth whoring
after English gods.
There is something to be said for exile:

you learn roots are deep.
That language is a tree, loses colour
under another sky.

The bark disappears with the snow,
and branches become hoarse.
However, the most reassuring thing

about the past is that it happened.
Dressed in tweeds or grey flannel,
its suburban pockets

bursting with immigrants—
'coloureds' is what they call us
over there—the city is no jewel, either:

lanes full of smoke and litter,
with puddles of unwashed
English children.

On New Year's Eve he heard an old man
at Trafalgar Square: 'It's no use trying
to change people. They'll be what they are.

An empire's last words are heard
on the hot sands of Africa.
The da Gamas, Clives, Dupleixs are back.

Victoria sleeps on her island
alone, an old hag,
shaking her invincible locks.'

Standing on Westminster Bridge,
it seemed the Thames had clogged
the chariot wheels of Boadicea to a stone.

Under the shadow of poplars
the river divides the city from the night.
The noises reappear,

of early trains, the milkman,
and the events of the day become
vocal in the newsboy.

2

Gulls wrinkle the air.
The boat heaves, opens the river's eye
in a twinkle of streets.

Houses drop into place.
The engine stops. From the funnel,
smoke balloons towards Ilhas.

I step out, and a *carreira*
takes me to the heart of Goa.
Echo of immaculate bells from hilltops

flagged with pale crosses.
Under the sun's oppressive glare
he stands alone

in a corner, an unrepentant schoolboy,
book in hand,
spanning an empire

from the Tagus to the China seas.
I stop to take a picture:
a storm of churches breaks about my eyes.

3

My tongue in English chains,
I return, after a generation, to you.
I am at the end

of my dravidic tether,
hunger for you unassuaged.
I falter, stumble.

Speak a tired language
wrenched from its sleep in the *Kural*,
teeth, palate, lips still new

to its agglutinative touch.
Now, hooked on celluloid, you reel
down plush corridors.

Commentary

Aranyani: Forest Spirit

Sanskrit is the 'Classical' language of the Indian subcontinent, the language of the early religious texts, of great epics such as the *Ramayana* and the *Mahabharata*, and of many plays and much poetry down to the medieval period. As a language it is closely related to ancient Greek, and the forerunner of many of the languages spoken in the northern part of the Subcontinent today, including Urdu, Hindi, Punjabi, Gujerati and Bengali, the five languages most widely spoken by Asians settled in Britain. All these languages belong to the 'Indo-European' language family, and are distantly related to English.

Ideas for discussion
Sanskrit came to the Subcontinent with the invaders who entered the country from the north, through the Khyber Pass, beginning in around 1000 BC. These people were cattle-rearing nomads (before their arrival there were already great cities in the valley of the Indus, in present-day Pakistan, at Harappa and Mohenjo-Daro). In this poem we can see the nomadic people turning to settlers, clearing the forests for farming, not unlike the Iron Age farmers who moved into Britain two thousand years ago.

Does this poem tell us anything about their attitude to the forest around their villages and farms?

Why is Aranyani 'served without tilling the ground'?

Could you relate this to the present-day destruction of forests and jungles over much of the world's surface?

Ideas for writing
Aranyani is the spirit of the forest. Try writing your own poem or description about the spirit of the woods or another place that you imagine might have a spirit, for example, the sea, sky, earth, river, mountain, city.

Nine Tamil Poems

Little or nothing is known about the individual poets who wrote these love lyrics but we do know that, of the poems in this selection, numbers 1, 3, 7 and 9 were written by women, the remainder by men.

Ideas for discussion

The speakers in these poems constitute a cast of characters, 'he', 'she' and 'her girl-friend' being the main ones. The poets assume these characters when they write. Have the men when writing always assumed a male character, and the women a female one? Tamil commentators who studied the anthology often arranged the poems in a sequence so as to tell a story. Can you see a narrative thread linking the poems as arranged here?

Could you work out a way of arranging them, or some of them, in a different sequence in order to tell a different story?

Ideas for writing

a These poems form a delicate sequence of images. Can you explain their appeal and effect? Write a detailed appreciation of the poems, dealing with the ideas and images of each individual poem; express your own feelings about them as a sequence.

b Add your own poem or poems to the sequence—perhaps by including more of the 'What he said' and 'What she said' type of poems. If you try this then you should aim to imitate the existing style— or you might attempt a more original approach by adding different characters, for example, 'What she said to her sister', 'What he said to his rival'.

Pather Panchali

Bibhutibhushan Banerji was born in 1894 in a village in Bengal and died in 1950. He earned his living principally as a schoolteacher and was the author of fifty books: novels and short story collections as well as travel books, translations, a Bengali grammar and books on astrology and the occult. But nothing else he wrote has won the popularity of Pather Panchali, now firmly established as a classic. Banerji's father, like Opu's in the book, earned a living as a family priest and singer of traditional songs. T. W. Clarke, one of the translators, suggests in his introduction, 'The author was able to live in Opu and make him so convincing because in a very true sense he was Opu. He tells us in one of his diaries that he modelled Shorbojoya on his own mother, both of whom bore the burden of crushing poverty. Mahananda Banerji, his father, was an unpractical scholar and dreamer, a man who in spite of obvious talents was found wanting in the ordinary duties of a father and husband'.

Notes
betel: a kind of leaf that is filled with spices and pieces of areca nut and chewed.
brahmin: a member of the Hindu priestly caste.

Ideas for discussion
In the first passage Banerji is trying to pinpoint the moment at which someone becomes aware of the power of literature for the first time. Notice how precise he is in describing physical sensations that gather around the experience. Why does he describe these sensations so clearly?

Can you suggest a reason why Opu identifies so strongly with the defeated hero Karna?

The *Mahabharata* is a great classic; here we see how it can appeal to a child. Opu has no books to read written specially for children, and no films, comic strips or TV programmes. But the events described here could be portrayed in a comic or on the screen (in fact, there is a successful series of comics on India based on this epic). What do the events described have in common with any comic stories you are familiar with?

In the second passage we see what happens when a child takes something literally, with, from his point of view, disastrous consequences. Many people find that smells bring back childhood memories more powerfully than anything else. Can you think of examples?

Why do you think Opu associates the smell of the book with his father?

Ideas for writing
a Opu is clearly a very imaginative boy who likes to fantasise and fill his mind from books. Continue the story by writing about another difficulty that he causes for himself because of his vivid imagination—be sure to bring in the other characters from the story.

b The extract shows how intense and exciting are the emotions of childhood. Spend some time thinking about your own memories of childhood and make some rough notes about what stands out for you from the past. Write about your own memories of childhood and what they mean to you. You might prefer to use your own imagination and to write a story about children and their imaginings.

c We all find it hard to write about the past, knowing where to begin and how to organise random memories. Where would you start? Some memories are stimulated by a particular sound, sight or even smell (think of the smell of the book in the passage). Try looking around the room until you see something that makes you think of a past event. Be prepared to spend a few minutes looking. Once you have been reminded of the past you may find that this memory leads on to another one and so on; after a few minutes of this *memory chain* make a note of all that you remember. One of these memories may be worth writing about in full.

Winter from the *Ramayana*

The *Ramayana*, composed by the legendary poet Valmiki, tells the story of Rama, his exile and subsequently his conquest of the mighty demon king Ravana who had captured Sita, Rama's wife and traditionally an ideal of Indian womanhood. The festival of Diwali, widely celebrated by Hindus in Britain, involves retelling episodes from this story.

Ideas for discussion
Much poetry is traditionally about the changing pattern of the seasons, with different times of year used to represent different moods or states of mind. In this and in the two poems that follow, Tagore's *Last Honey* and Rafat's *Arrival of the Monsoon*, we can see how, in the Subcontinent's very different climate, seasons represent different moods and feelings. The poet of the Ramayana is describing winter in northern India—what does the season mean to him?

Ideas for writing
Winter, Last Honey and Arrival of the Monsoon

a Each of these poems celebrates the arrival and departure of particular times and seasons. Write your own poem or description about a time of the year that you especially appreciate. Try to include precise details involving all your senses and write so that someone from a different part of the world, who perhaps knows nothing of your seasons, could appreciate and understand what you have written.

b Each writer has taken great care to give us a clear image of their chosen time—write an appreciation of one or more of the poems and explain in detail how each writer creates the atmosphere and beauty of their particular time. If you write about more than one poem you could include the similarities and differences you notice in the way they describe their seasons.

Last Honey

Rabindranath Tagore was born in 1861 and died in 1941. He was the winner of the Nobel Prize for Literature in 1913. He was a leading figure in the Indian Independence movement; a writer of outstanding fiction and plays as well as poetry; a painter, educator and musician.

Notes
sajne, akanda: flowering trees.
dolan-cãpã: a flowering bush that blooms in spring.

Points for discussion
The extract from the *Ramayana* (p. 21) shows how winter did not mean the same to a poet writing in north India as it would mean to a poet writing in northern Europe. The difference is more marked in *Last Honey*. What is the meaning of the onset of *Baisakh* for Tagore?

Radice, the translator, writes that the poem has 'a strange, bitter-sweet, ambiguous tone' and suggests that this is connected with Tagore's sense of growing older. Can you see what he means? There are images of barrenness and death in the poem, but does the poem, and the movement of the lines strike you as pessimistic or depressed?

Ideas for writing
For ideas for writing turn to page 138.

Arrival of the Monsoon

Taufiq Rafat is a contemporary poet from Pakistan. His work has been published along with that of two other Pakistani poets who write in English, Kaleem Omar and Maki Kureishi, in *Wordfall* (1975).

Ideas for discussion
The monsoon rains are literally life-giving as if they fail the harvest will be affected and there will not be enough to eat. Traditionally in poetry the rainy season is the season for love. So heavy rain has a different significance from what it might have in England. How does Rafat convey the sense of movement and energy connected with the rain?

He writes 'All the sounds we have loved are restored.' What sort of sounds is he thinking of?

In your own words, what does the monsoon rain mean to him?

Ideas for writing
For ideas for writing turn to page 138.

Village Without Walls

Vyankatesh Madgulkar was born in 1927 in Maharashtra. After involvement in the Quit India movement during the last years of British rule, he began to publish short stories. He wrote screenplays in the early fifties for a Bombay film company and since 1955 has worked for All India Radio.

Notes
dhoti: garment worn by some Hindu men and boys, consisting of an unstitched length of cloth fastened round the waist.

Ideas for discussion
To people living as close as these villagers to the margins of poverty, failure to plough and sow your piece of land can mean disaster. The village in this novel is shown to be completely self-contained (this would be less the case today). The teacher is a representative—the only one—of the world beyond the village. What expectations do the villagers have of him? Are they realistic ones?

What are their real needs and what sort of education might be most useful to them?

Ideas for writing
a Imagine that you are a journalist travelling through the country and that you arrive in the village in the evening of this eventful day; you hear about this story and realise that your paper would be interested in such an unusual event. Write the whole story and include some interviews with the main characters and with people from other villages, not all of whom would have approved of what happened.

b Some readers would be surprised by the story because it was a woman who achieved the feat of strength. Write your own story about a woman or girl who achieves something that surprises her community. You might prefer to write about your own knowledge of similar 'surprises' or to put forward your views about why people should not be amazed by such events.

I Left You Behind

Dawood Haider was born in Bangladesh in 1951 and while still a student began to publish collections of his poetry.

Ideas for discussion

We hear a lot, in the media and elsewhere, about the growing cities of the 'Third World'. This poem may help to bring those statistics alive. Do you think there are any parallels between the situation described in this poem and life in contemporary Britain? Can you think of different circumstances in which people move about in search of work?

At the end of the third verse the narrator says 'But I did not say / or do any of those things': Why not?

Ideas for writing

Big Brother and I Left You Behind

a Write a letter home from any one of the characters in the poem or the story in which he explains what has been happening to him and how he feels about it. You could include a reply if you feel confident enough about what you imagine it would be like.

b Leaving home and being separated from those we love are powerful and universal themes. Write your own poem or story on these themes. You could attempt to write about a situation or place quite different to your own to see if you can create a convincing sense of what someone else's experiences might be like whilst showing how universal the themes are.

Big Brother

Shekhar Joshi was born in Almora, a town that features in this story, in 1934 and lives in Allahabad, where he works as a technical supervisor. Many of his stories, like this one, feature urban industrial life; a collection of them was published in 1958.

Notes

Sahab: Sir.

Babu: a term of respect; added to Jagdish's name it indicates the difference in status between him and the boy serving in the café.

Ideas for discussion

Jagdish Babu and Madan have both left their village and come to work in the city, but in different circumstances. Jagdish probably works in an office; Madan is only nine or ten but already has to earn his living working in a café. Madan's liveliness is described as being 'like a drop of water sliding along the leaf of a lotus' (the lotus features often in traditional poetry). How is his liveliness demonstrated early on in the story? Why does Jagdish feel lonely?

The Subcontinent is having to experience massive social and industrial change, such as has taken place in Europe over the last couple of centuries, in a very short time. What evidence of this change is there in the passage?

Ideas for writing
For ideas for writing see above.

An Introduction

Kamala Das was born in Malabar in 1934 and now lives in Bombay. She has published collections of poetry written in English, as well as prose fiction in Malayalam. Many of her poems deal with the pains and trials of love relationships; in others she evokes her childhood with passionate nostalgia. In her autobiography *My Life* (1975), she writes about her family of poets and scholars, among them her mother, who was a poet.

Ideas for discussion
Kamala Das gives a powerful description of the struggles she has experienced growing up among people who have differing and sometimes conflicting expectations of her. What expectations do other people have of her? She describes being criticized for writing in English, 'not your mother tongue'. In what way might the same conflict present itself to someone growing up in Britain?

As well as clothes—the traditional sari or 'western' shirt and trousers—roles can be represented by names. Amy, as an English name, represents the westernised side of her. Kamala is a very common Indian name. Madhavikutty is a pen-name she had used when writing in Malayalam. Madhavi is the 'shakti'—female form—of Madhave, Master of Knowledge, one of the names of the deities Vishnu and Krishna. So it is a name that connects her to poetic and scholarly traditions in her own family. Is it possible to move from one role or identity into another, as you choose to or need to? Think of occasions in your life when you change roles. Are you the same at home as you are at school?

Ideas for writing

In the poem the writer tries to deal with the difficulties of having to fit into a role that the family, and society in general, believes to be appropriate. We all know that conforming with other people's ideas of what is right is often impossible. Write your own piece about the problems of remaining an individual under all the pressures that there are to give in to convention.

Muniyakka

Lakshmi Kannan was born in 1947 and she writes in both Tamil and English. She is a poet, critic and translator as well as a writer of fiction, and works as a University teacher.

Notes

rangoli: decorative pattern made on freshly-swept and moistened earth at the threshold of a house.

jaggery: brown sugar often made from the sap of a palm tree.

areca nut: shavings of this nut are chewed with the betel leaf.

dhavshma of Kali: Kali is a female counterpart to the god Siva, a goddess of power in its frightening and destructive aspect. The dhavshma of Kali represents her rampage of destruction.

kum kum: vermilion powder applied to images as part of worship.

turmeric: a bright yellow spice also used as a dye.

ajji: grandmother.

toddy: alcoholic drink made from the sap of certain kinds of palm tree.

bidi: a kind of cigarette.

Bairappa's leaf: in South India it is the custom to serve food on large leaves.

Ideas for discussion

Throughout the story we are made aware that Muniyakka is not just the crazy old lady she appears to be. She is the sort of person who, in times past in Europe, might have been stigmatized as a witch. As it is, the people of her home village 'always described ghosts and devils like this, essentially in their female form'. Can you suggest any reasons why this should be so? Does the story suggest any reasons?

Muniyakka appears to be a devotee of the goddess Kali. She pours scorn on all social conventions. What is it about her 'queer humour', do you think, that Mrs Rao finds enjoyable?

Why is she so careful to observe such rituals as the *sraddha*, in view of her feelings about her husband? (You might think about the purposes of a ritual, as much for the person carrying it out as for the person on whose behalf it is performed.)

What is the 'subtle transformation' that shows on Muniyakka's face after she has completed the *sraddha*? How is she shown to be a marginal sort of person, with no proper social status?

Ideas for writing

a The story is partly about being individual, even eccentric and strange. Write a poem or story about an unusual and unconventional character; you could describe someone you know. You could write in a

143

more general way, in essay form, about individuality itself.

b In *Muniyakka* we have a very detailed picture of an eccentric old woman. What kind of person do you think she is and what is the author trying to show us about people, and especially about the lives of women, through the careful description that we have?

Across the Black Waters

Mulk Raj Anand is a leading English-language novelist, with a prolific output. He was born in 1905 in Peshawar (now in Pakistan) and was educated in the Punjab, and in Cambridge and Paris. In his Introduction Peter Traves discusses some of the reasons that lay behind Anand's decision to write in English. His first novel *Untouchable* (1935) described a day in the life of a Sweeper, and broke new ground in its frank and humane portrayal of characters from the very poorest levels of society. *Across the Black Waters* is the second part of a trilogy of novels. The first, *The Village* (1939), shows Lalu growing up in a Sikh village in the Punjab, and portrays a traditional peasant way of life. Lalu challenges the accepted order in the village, is forced to leave home, joins the army and finds himself fighting on the Western Front. In the third part of the trilogy, *The Sword and the Sickle* (1942) he is back in India and involved in the Independence struggle.

Notes

Havildar: Sergeant.
Jemadar: Lieutenant.
Lance-Naik: Lance-Corporal.
gora: white man.
Karnel, Ajitan: Colonel, Adjutant.

The term '*sarkar*' refers to the British and '*to eat the salt of the sarkar*' means to take an oath of allegiance to the British crown.

Ideas for discussion

'Going over the top'—the moment when the soldiers must climb out of their trenches and move into the attack—has been described by many British writers. Here we see it from an Indian point of view. As well as providing a graphic account of battle, this passage explores some of the issues of duty and loyalty confronting these soldiers. They have only a hazy idea of why the war is being fought. Would British and French soldiers have had any better idea? Havildar Lachman Singh experiences a conflict of duty when he wonders what to tell his men about the lack of artillery support for their action. The Indian troops want to demonstrate they are the equals of the British (where are the British shown to be playing on this?), but they feel they have been betrayed. What effect could this have on their attitude to the British rulers in India?

Would the spectacle of British and German soldiers slaughtering each other in such numbers in the name of civilisation change their attitude to Europeans in general? What do you think their attitude would be?

The first World War generated much literature of protest and it may be that Anand was thinking of the English poet Wilfred Owen when he called his British Officer Owen. What can you gather of Owen's attitude to the war from this passage?

How would you describe the relationship between Owen and Lalu in this passage? You could compare Anand's writing to some British writers of the period—Owen, Sassoon, or Graves in his autobiography *Goodbye to All That*.

Ideas for writing

a Write a letter from one of the soldiers to his family at home in which he describes the attack and what happened.

b The extract deals with the demands of loyalty and honour placed on the Indian soldiers in this strange environment. Write a series of entries for a diary of one of the soldiers in which he records the experiences of the war, his feelings about them and his attitude to the idea of fighting in what is really someone else's war.

Jejuri

Arun Kolatkar was born in 1932. He was educated at Bombay University, and now lives in Bombay where he works as a graphic artist. *Jejuri* was awarded the Commonwealth Poetry Prize in 1976. Kolatkar writes poetry in Marathi as well as English and has contributed to many magazines and anthologies.

Notes
Maruti: a god of the winds.

Ideas for discussion
The visitor does not visit the temples as a pilgrim, nor yet exactly as a tourist. It is his own cultural heritage he is experiencing and the poet

recognises the sacredness of the place. At the same time his attitude is sceptical and ironic; can you see examples of this in these poems? In *Heart of Ruin*, how does he celebrate the natural life that goes on in the ruins of one of the temples? He says it is 'no more a place of worship'— so what does he mean when he calls it 'nothing less than the house of god'?

The Priest's Son and *The Butterfly* stand next to each other in the sequence. There is an obvious narrative connection between them. A number of poems in the sequence describes the people who live among the temples, rather as the animals do, as if both were inhabiting a natural landscape. What is the attitude of the priest's son to the traditional stories?

Hills paints a vivid word-picture of the five hills which, according to legend, are the demons Khandoba killed. Can you think of any stories in British folklore that explain natural features in this way?

Ideas for writing

a Each of the poems looks at a particular aspect of the area in detail: the ruined temple, the boy's description, the butterfly and the hills. Write several poems of your own that describe aspects of a particular area or place; give each poem an individual style whilst keeping some elements in common.

b Imagine you are a visitor to a place that is special or holy to some people but not to you; describe your feelings as you look around and try to understand what makes this place so important for others.

An Autobiography

Gandhi was born in 1869 and was assassinated by Hindu extremists as India gained independence in 1947. He is one of the great figures in twentieth-century politics, as much for his advocacy of non-violence as for his specific role in the struggle to win independence from the British. His life was the subject of a widely-shown film made by Richard Attenborough and released in 1984. His autobiography gives us the opportunity to read about his life in his own words.

Ideas for discussion

Gandhi went to South Africa as a lawyer, to act in a particular case, and not with any overtly political purpose. Can you see any signs of the courage and persistence he was to display later in his career?

While he is spending a freezing night on the station, having been thrown off the train because he refuses to travel in the luggage van, he wonders where his duty lies. What courses of action are open to him?

What would be the easiest thing for him to do? Is there anything in his reflections at this point that foreshadows his creed of non-violence, and refusal to seek vengeance? When he gets to Johannesburg and tells Sheth Abdul Gani what has happened, the latter replies 'This country is not for men like you'. What does he mean by this?

When Gandhi decides to travel the last part of his journey by train first class why does he wear 'faultless European dress' when going to buy his ticket?

Ideas for writing

a Continue the story for another day or two—you may need to invent new characters and places but try to stick closely to the style of the original.

b Gandhi is a name that most people have heard of for a variety of reasons and his life story has become better known because of the film made about him; the film uses quite a lot of material from the Autobiography. Choose someone you have heard of, Gandhi himself perhaps, and write a brief biography of that person giving some idea of what makes her or him important to you. It would be especially appropriate to choose someone who was involved in the history of India or Pakistan. Avoid simply copying out chunks from another book. If you want to use material from other books put it in quotation marks and say where it came from.

c Gandhi says he sent a 'long telegram' to complain of the treatment he received on the train, a letter to a friend describing what happened on the coach, and a 'note' to the station-master, announcing his intention of buying a first class ticket. Write the telegram, the letter and the note as you think Gandhi might have written them.

Wedding in the Flood

Taufiq Rafat is a contemporary poet from Pakistan. His work has been published along with that of two other Pakistani poets who write in English, Kaleem Omar and Maki Kureishi, in *Wordfall* (1975).

Notes

palankeen: a covered litter carried by four men in which the bride sits.
that girl has been licking too many pots: this refers to a Punjabi saying that if a girl is in the habit of licking the cooking-pots, it will rain on her wedding day.
her henna-ed hands: this refers to the custom of decorating the bride's hands with patterns (called *mendi*), drawn in henna.

147

Commentary

Ideas for discussion

This is a traditional village wedding. It will have been arranged between the two families and, we can infer, when the groom says 'If only her face matches her hands', that the couple will not have met before the ceremony. Such a wedding is a sad event as well as a happy one; traditionally the bride leaves her home and goes to live with her in-laws. Tensions can develop between the bride and her mother-in-law, hence the groom's comment that he hopes she will give him no 'mother-in-law problems'. Another source of tension may be the size of the dowry provided by the father when the daughter marries, and which can make the marriage of daughters an expensive business.

The poem conveys a picture of the day's events from four different points of view: the bride's mother, the bride, the groom, the groom's father. Each has different expectations and preoccupations: what are they?

The poem opens 'They are taking my girl away for ever'. By the end of the poem this line has come to have an added meaning.

How does the poem use repetition to create a sense of mounting threat?

Ideas for writing

What makes this an unusual poem is the way the different viewpoint of each character is put forward. Try writing a poem, or story, of your own, in which several characters who are part of the same event all see it in differing ways. There are many events that you could choose from; a family event could be a suitable one, for example, a party, funeral, festival.

Pratidwandi

Sunil Gangopadhyay was born in 1934 and educated in Calcutta. He is an outstanding poet as well as a writer of fiction. In the sixties he edited a literary magazine, *Kritibash*, around which were gathered a lot of new talents, and which formed links with American writers of the time such as Allen Ginsberg. *Pratidwandi* has been made into a film by the great Bengali director Satyajit Ray.

Notes

the family idol: many Hindu homes have a room, or part of a room, set aside for worship, with a shrine.
he bent down and touched her feet: a traditional mark of respect.
a Madrasi fellow: someone from Madras (in south India).
darwan: doorkeeper.

aaplog aisi chillanessey . . .: 'Don't shout so much or everything will be closed. Just keep your mouths shut.'
Chowringhee: a district of Calcutta.

Ideas for discussion
Pratidwandi was made into a film. How would you turn this extract into a powerful episode in the film? What images would you focus on? What are the feelings Siddhartha has towards his mother at the beginning of the passage and then at the end? What do you make of his evasive replies to her enquiries after the interview?

What do his feelings about the applicant with the stammer tell us about him?

Why are the candidates being interviewed in English?

How does the mood of the applicants change as the day progresses? Why does Siddhartha feel so helplessly angry? Why is his anger described as useless?

Ideas for writing
a Imagine that Siddhartha meets the young man with the stammer a couple of days later. Write their conversation about what happened on their interview day.
b You may think that Siddhartha was right to have become so angry at the treatment that he and the other young men received or you may feel that he was foolishly impatient. Write a story of your own which illustrates how you think people should behave under trying circumstances.

Master Babu

Kaiser Haq is a poet and translator from Bangladesh. He has published two collections of poems and has studied at universities in Bangladesh and Britain. He is now Assistant Professor of English at Dhaka University. He has translated the poems of Shamsur Rahman, a leading contemporary Bengali poet.

Notes
dal: a dish made from lentils

Ideas for discussion
It is easy to make fun of varieties of spoken English other than those we use ourselves. This poem invites us to look at what can lie behind such laughter. The Bengalis were the first to experience contact with the English language and to be educated in it. The term 'Babu' originally

meant something like 'Mister' or 'Esquire'. It came to mean a clerk (see, for example, the extract from Anand's *Across the Black Waters*), and was on occasion used by the British as a term of ridicule directed at Indians who were felt to be getting 'above themselves'.

Many Indians were obliged to use English under British rule; at the same time reading English gave them wider access to current ideas concerning national liberation and political freedom. At what point does the teacher's English break down and why?

He is shown to prefer the longer, more elaborate word to the simpler one—'maintain silence', for example, instead of 'keep quiet'. Why is this?

Why is he such a sad figure?

What are the different kinds of English people feel it is appropriate to use in different situations?

Ideas for writing

a Write a description or poem about one or more of your teachers. What do you think they are like at home as well as in school?

b Master Babu makes his living from teaching people how to speak and write a foreign language properly. Do you think there is one way to speak and write English? Should everyone who learns English speak in exactly the same way? What are your feelings and views about the way language should be taught and used?

Circus Cat Alley Cat

Anita Desai was born in 1937 in Delhi; she now lives in Bombay. Her father was German and her mother was Bengali. Her fiction is widely published in Britain as well as India. A recent novel, *In Custody*, describes the complicated relationship that develops between an elderly Urdu poet and a young admirer of his poetry. Anita Desai also writes for children; *Village by the Sea* describes upheavals in a fishing village undergoing industrial development, and the impact of this on the lives of two children.

Notes

Malabar: a region of south-west India, where circus families are traditionally said to come from.

Ideas for discussion

As you read the story, do you find yourself assuming that the narrator is female? If so, why? Does it matter?

Why do you think the narrator identifies so strongly with Anna the circus performer? (One minute she is the trainer, the next minute she is the cat.)

At the end of the story, the narrator says 'But throughout the performance, the thought uppermost in my mind was: where is Anna's husband?' Why do you think she is so obsessed by this?

Ideas for writing

a The circus is a very atmospheric place. Write a story or description about a visit to the circus and try to create a sense of the sights and sounds there.

b How do you feel about the use of animals in the circus; do you think they enjoy their performances or is it all cruelty? Write an essay in which you put forward your feelings. You might include other uses of animals too, such as farming, experiments, hunting.

Of Mothers among other things and Self-Portrait

A. K. Ramanujan was born in south India in 1929. Following an academic career in India he became Professor of Dravidian Studies and Linguistics at the University of Chicago in 1962. He is well-known as both a poet writing in English and as a translator (his versions of some ancient Tamil poems are on pages 7–11).

Ideas for discussion

Ramanujan describes how his mother is bent with age but still, when she sees a single grain of rice on the floor, she must bend down to pick it up. Why does his mouth suddenly go dry when he sees his mother bent down to pick up a single grain of rice?

What are the 'other things' referred to in the title?

In *Self-Portrait* he describes the shock of glimpsing his face unexpectedly in a shop window; why does he feel so startled? Why does he say the portrait he imagines he sees is '*signed* by my father'?

Ideas for writing

Write a brief, concentrated poem describing yourself or someone that you know very well. You could start by noting down as many ideas as you can about them and then select the details that seem especially important. Think about how the author has selected particular points about his mother and himself.

Roots and Shadows

Shashi Deshpande was born near Bombay, where she now lives. She has been writing seriously since 1975 and has published collections of short stories and some children's stories, among them *The Narayanpur Incident* (1982), which is based on an incident in the Indian Independence Struggle. As well as *Roots and Shadows*, which appeared in 1983, she has published *The Dark Holds No Terrors* (1980), a study of a woman freeing herself from a disastrous marriage.

Notes
champak: a tree with golden yellow flowers.

paan, supari: paan is the betel leaf which is filled with spices and shavings from the areca nut (here called supari) and chewed especially after meals. The two women are cleaning the leaves and preparing the areca nut.

gotras: family groups, clans.

Ideas for discussion
Indu describes arriving as a 'fifteen-days-old motherless infant'; one of the functions of the type of 'extended family' described here is to be able to cope with such a situation, as in the society where such a family emerges there are no social services to fall back on. Here and elsewhere in the novel a sort of balance sheet is drawn up for this kind of family and the arranged marriages that sustain it. What are the benefits of this kind of family? What are the drawbacks? When arranging a marriage in the traditional way, many things have to be taken into account. Do the two families like and respect one another? Do the man and the woman come from the same community and background? Horoscopes may have to be worked out to see if they match. In the second passage Indu describes some of the feelings the prospective bride may experience. What are these feelings?

Indu's attempts to provoke Mini into thinking about her future are not very successful. Why is this? Why does Mini say at one point: 'You think the most peculiar thoughts, Indu. What's the point of thinking such things?'

What is the significance of the words Indu called out in her sleep: 'it's not fair. It's not fair'?

What does Indu mean by her expression 'Marriage as a catalyst'?

Ideas for writing

a Continue the story and write the scene in which Indu announces her decision about the house and Mini's marriage to the other characters, giving her reasons for her choice.

b Indu is clearly a modern woman who has rejected certain traditional ideas about a woman's place; Mini, however, appears to accept the basic view that a woman's place is very much in the home. Think through your own views about this. Write an essay about this topic setting out your thoughts and feelings. Your title could be simply *A woman's place?*

Breaking Stones

Nirala was the pen name of the Hindi poet Suryakant Tripathi, born in 1896 in Bengal. Originally a student of Bengali, he learnt Hindi after his marriage under the influence of his wife. He wrote fiction and essays as well as poetry and edited two literary journals.

Notes

choli: a kind of blouse worn with a sari.
sitar: a stringed musical instrument.

Ideas for discussion

It is interesting to see how much drama Nirala succeeds in creating from this fleeting and wordless encounter. What is the significance of the 'long rows of trees' and 'high-walled mansions' in this context?

Does the poem only express admiration for the woman's toughness or is there more than that to the poet's attitudes and feelings about her?

What do you think is the 'strain of music' he heard, 'as if from a tuned sitar'?

Ideas for writing

The woman in the poem becomes a symbol, representing something about women; what do you think she stands for? Try writing your own piece about a single figure completing one particular action that suggests a specific idea or theme. You may need to work on several versions of this before you feel it is right.

The Only American From Our Village

Arun Joshi was born in 1939. He was educated in India and the USA and now lives in New Delhi where he is Executive Director of the Shri Ram Centre for Industrial Relations and Human Resources. He has published four novels as well as collections of short stories. His powerful short novel *The Apprentice* (1974) deals with an incident of corruption in post-Independent India, contrasted with the idealism of the Independence movement.

Notes
bidi: a kind of cigarette.

Ideas for discussion

There is something frightening about the quiet persistent way in which the *ashtamp farosh* tells his story. Obviously nothing is going to stop him. Yet at times he almost seems to be talking to himself. What effect is created by his silences, and then his sudden unexpected questions: 'Did you send him a ticket?' for example.

What are the small details that show how far Dr Khanna has come from his origins? What do the presents Dr Khanna brings with him say about his attitude to his family?

Dr Khanna has enjoyed opportunities that his father never had, although the latter was an outstanding student. Why do you think the old man went back, that last time, to see his old school?

Why did he insist on walking barefoot over the burning sand? Does the manner of his death strike you as tragic, or grotesque, or both?

The author writes of Dr Khanna's reaction to this part of the story 'Dr Khanna winced but his training in the new civilisation had been perfect.' What does he mean?

The breakdown of traditional family patterns is a theme of much contemporary South Asian writing, and of much British writing as well. The distance that opens up as a result of education has been a theme of British novelists, and playwrights and poets (John Osborne, David Storey, Tony Harrison for instance) over the last thirty years. In this story it is not so much a breakdown in communication, as a neglect of family duties; in this case the duty of a son to care for his father in old age. Do you think such distances and such misunderstandings are inevitable today? Is anyone to blame? Try imagining the whole story from Dr Khanna's point of view. How different would it be?

Ideas for writing

a Although the story is told by the old man alone we are able to build up a strong picture of each of the characters. Write a study of the story, explaining what you feel the author was trying to show us and paying particular attention to the characters. Describe what each one was like, the part they play in the story and include your feelings towards them.

b Dr Khanna discovers that your past will catch up with you in the most unlikely ways. Write your own story about a character who undergoes a similar experience.

c Imagine that you are Dr Khanna; write your account of your relationship with your father and your struggle to succeed in America. You could take the opportunity to defend the way you behaved and describe how you feel now.

I Am Not That Woman

Kishwar Naheed was born in 1940 and educated at Punjab University. She is Director of Lahore Arts Council in Pakistan as well as a journalist, translator and broadcaster.

Ideas for discussion

Kishwar Naheed makes an impassioned plea against the oppression of women. Why would she not wish to be equated with the woman on the poster? It is important to emphasize that the woman on the poster 'half-naked, selling you shoes and socks' might seem to some people to represent the modern world. In a society where ideas of female modesty are very strict, such a poster could appear to stand for new freedoms, progress, a kind of modernization which in some people's minds is equated with westernization. Would such a poster have the same significance in Britain?

'A nation of captive minds / cannot be free' she writes. What are the social or political implications of these lines?

What might she mean when she says she can 'walk on water / when I am drowning'?

She writes 'You traded in / my chastity, my motherhood, my loyalty'? What does this mean? How could it be connected with the woman in the advertisement?

Ideas for writing

I Am Not That Woman, The Twelfth Man and A Prison Nightfall

a These three poems form an interesting group. Each poem has a strong statement to make about life and each is quite individual in the way it is written; yet they also share something because each one is a comment on the way we view life. Write an appreciation of the three poems, dealing with each one separately, but also comparing the way they are written and the ideas that they contain.

b Each poem makes a strong personal statement about the writer's view of life. Choose a subject that you feel very strongly about and use one of the poems as a model or example through which to express your views.

The Twelfth Man

Iftikhar Arif was born in Lucknow in 1943. In Pakistan he was well-known as a poet and broadcaster; he now lives in London where he is the director of *Urdu Markaz*, a literary organisation catering for Urdu literature in Britain. *Urdu Markaz* organises many events including the traditional *mushaira*, a poetry recital or symposium that can attract very large audiences. The existence of such an organisation makes the point that there are now many poets settled in Britain who write in a variety of South Asian languages, together with various organisations and publications that have arisen to foster these activities.

Ideas for discussion

Iftikhar Arif takes the idea of the twelfth man from cricket; the player who is picked for the team as a substitute. Half in and half out of the team, he will only get to play 'when disaster strikes' (literally, when someone is sick or injured), and he may spend the whole of the game as a spectator. Why does he feel 'separate and alone' as he salutes the twelfth man?

The poem evokes a common fantasy of unexpectedly being called on, and saving the day—scoring the winning goal or the winning run. Does the poem have anything to say about fame (or notoriety) in the modern world? (The American artist Andy Warhol said that in the future everyone would have a chance to be famous for two minutes.)

What does Iftikhar Arif mean by the 'game' here? Why is the player's relationship with it 'lifelong'?

Is the 'calamity' he evokes towards the end of the poem something that will come to all of us in the end?

Ideas for writing

For ideas for writing see pages 155–6.

A Prison Nightfall

Faiz Ahmad Faiz was born in Sialkot in the Punjab and was at various times teacher, journalist, army officer and broadcaster. He was imprisoned in Pakistan in connection with his political and trade union activities and lived for some time in exile in Beirut. His poems reached a very wide audience and his *gazals*, or short verses, were sung by the most popular singers of the day.

Ideas for discussion
A Prison Nightfall is autobiographical, clearly related to time Faiz spent in prison. The translator Mahmood Jamal writes of his work: 'His strength lay in the subtle blending of romance and idealism, simple diction and accessible images, and, above all, in his desire to reach the masses and his concern for humanity. He hardly ever wrote free verse and maintained a certain rhythm and metre, often using the *gazal* to convey a political message as no poet had done before him.' The poem reminds us that the night sky, moon and stars are more spectacular in the Subcontinent than in northern Europe. What do you think are the traditional poetic elements in this poem?

Why are the trees in the prison yard 'homeless'?

Some of the imagery you might expect to find in a pop song or a ballad; is it surprising to find it in a political poem about imprisonment? What is the effect of it being used in this way?

Ideas for writing
For ideas for writing see pages 155–6.

A Horse and Two Goats

R. K. Narayan was born in Madras in 1907 and later settled in the small town of Mysore which, under the name of Malgudi, became the setting for most of his novels. Narayan's mother-tongue is Tamil, like Muni in this story, but Narayan has always written in English. Apart from a brief spell as a teacher he has always earned his living as a writer and he has been widely published in Britain. Narayan is a humane and humorous writer, deeply attached to Indian social and spiritual traditions, but not in any fanatical spirit. As well as many novels and short stories he has published an autobiography *My Days* (1975).

Notes
Swarga: paradise.   *bhang:* marijuana.
betel: a leaf that is covered with pieces of nut and spices and chewed.

dhobi: washerman.

Shiva, Vishnu: together with Brahman, the three deities of the Hindu trinity.

namaste: traditional form of greeting.

Bhagwan: Blessed one.

Pongal: harvest time, harvest festival.

Parangi: foreigner.

avatar: manifestation of a deity on earth.

pundit: learned person, teacher.

collector: during the time of British rule, the collector was the chief administrative official of a district.

Kali Yuga: the age of lead, the worst age in the Hindu cycle of time; an age of moral decline.

lakh: 10,000

puja room: room (or part of a room) in a Hindu home set aside for worship.

Yama Loka: the Lord of the Dead.

Ideas for discussion

The humour of *A Horse and Two Goats* lies partly in the way the American's and Muni's way of life are laid side by side without any comment. Each describes his life in a self-absorbed way as if everything he says and does is the most normal thing in the world. Yet if Muni could understand what the American was saying, it would sound as extraordinary to him as his stories of the Avatars and his theatrical exploits would sound to the American. What is the effect of the American's opening question: 'Is there a gas station near here?' Muni's first reaction when he encounters the American is to feel guilty. In view of what takes place why is this ironic?

The American's offer of money is no doubt well-intentioned; could it be construed as insulting? The American assumes the statue belongs to Muni and is for sale; is there a tendency for tourists to make assumptions like this?

Muni is dominated by his wife and obliged to adopt a subservient attitude towards the shopman; ironically it is only with the American that he can really let himself go—and the American cannot understand a word he says. Why should he think it would be such a good idea to tape Muni?

Muni is poor, even by the standards of his village, but is he lacking in human or cultural resources? (For more about the Ramayana and the Mahabharata see pages 135, 138 and 137.) The Tamil Muni speaks is especially fine, and while the village is only a 'speck', the name Kritam we are told means 'crown'. Is it Narayan's intention to make fun of the village's pretensions?

Ideas for writing
a Continue the story for either one or both of the characters. How would Muni explain the disappearance of the horse and the appearance of his sudden wealth to the rest of the villagers? What would the American tell his friends when he shows them his horse?

b The story is based on a simple misunderstanding but a very revealing and funny one. Try writing a story of your own in which such a misunderstanding takes place.

Rough Passage
Rajgopal Parthasarathy was born in south India in 1934 and educated in Bombay; he has also studied at Leeds University. He was a lecturer in English Literature in Bombay for ten years before joining the Indian branch of the Oxford University Press. He edited *Ten Twentieth Century Indian Poets* (1976), an anthology of contemporary poetry written in English.

Notes
Ravi Shankar: Indian musician especially popular in Britain in the sixties.

Clive: leading figure in the establishment of British power in India through the East India Company. He was born in 1725 and died, probably by his own hand, after being accused of corruption, in 1774.

Dupleix: (1697–1763) Governor-General of the French Indies, that is the French possessions in India.

my dravidic tether: 'Dravidian' refers to the people and culture of south India.

Kural: anthology of ancient Tamil love poetry (for translations of some of the poems, see *Nine Tamil Poems*, page 7).

Ideas for discussion
Parthasarathy's first poem describes London and student life in the sixties. Do you think London was in some ways not what Parthasarathy expected it to be, or what his fellow-Indians back home think it is?

What did he learn about himself and his own cultural heritage through being 'in exile'?

What picture of Britain emerges from the last six stanzas of the first section?

The second section paints a vivid picture of Goa with its many churches. Most of the population of this former Portuguese colony are still Catholic (there are other Christian communities in India going back to the 8th century). At its height the Portuguese Empire stretched from the Tagus, the river on which Lisbon stands, to the 'China Seas'. 'Agglutinative' in the third section printed here refers to the structure of the Tamil language; agglutinative languages are those that function by forming long words out of lots of simple or root words.

Ideas for writing

a Write about the advantages and difficulties, as you have experienced them or as you can imagine them, of growing up in two cultures, speaking two languages.

b Write the conversations that take place between somebody who, like Parthasarathy, has just come back from studying abroad for some years, and members of his or her family.

Ideas for Coursework

1 The anthology contains an extensive range of poems dealing with all sorts of subjects. Select the ones that you enjoyed the most and write an appreciative essay about what you enjoyed.

2 Many of the poems in the collection deal with the natural world in a variety of ways. Write an essay about what you learned of the natural world in South Asia through these poems. Some poems that you might include would be *Aranyani, Winter, Last Honey, Arrival of the Monsoon, Wedding in the Flood, Breaking Stones, Jejuri* and *A Prison Nightfall*.

3 If you were asked to select just two poems from the collection, which would you choose and why? There could be many ways of deciding this. Think about what the basis for your choice would be before you select.

4 The anthology may have created an interest for you in one or more of the poets represented. Use the suggested reading list and read more poems by the author of your choice and then write an essay on his or her poetry.

5 Imagine that you have been asked to record a radio programme about South Asian Literature; the programme is to be a mixture of readings from this anthology and of comments and information. Work with some others, if possible, and prepare and tape the programme that you would like to broadcast.

6 A number of the pieces in the anthology deal with the problems of people having to leave their homes to find work or of finding themselves in a place where they do not feel really accepted or at home. Look at some of these pieces again and then write about what they make you feel, and think about the difficulties of people in such situations. Some possible pieces to include are, *I Left You Behind, Big Brother, Across The Black Waters, An Autobiography, The Only American From Our Village, Roots and Shadows, Rough Passage*.

7 A number of pieces in the anthology feature women in a variety of roles and situations. Select some of those that you found the most interesting and comment on what they made you think about the position of women generally. Be careful to consider the differences between the situations of the women described. You will find the notes

on each piece very helpful here. Some titles to look at include *Nine Poems, Village Without Walls, An Introduction, Muniyakki, Circus Cat Alley Cat, Of Mothers, Roots and Shadows, Breaking Stones, I Am Not That Woman* and *A Horse and Two Goats.*

8 Imagine that a number of the women from the anthology met together to discuss their feelings and experiences, perhaps at a conference of some kind. Write their conversations.

9 Many pieces in the collection focus on family life, its pleasures and its pains. What did you find interesting about the way family life was presented? You could look simply at the various families described in the anthology and then consider their similarities and differences. You might prefer to discuss what you have noticed about family life in South Asia, bearing in mind what a huge area it is! A final suggestion would be to choose two or three families to discuss in detail where there is a particular point of comparison, for example, marriage, inheritance. Some suitable titles include *Nine Tamil Poems, Pather Panchali, Village Without Walls, I Left You Behind, Big Brother, Muniyakka, Wedding in the Flood, Pratidwandi, Circus Cat Alley Cat, Roots and Shadows, The Only American From Our Village* and *A Horse and Two Goats.*

10 Several pieces deal with individuals at moments of crisis in their lives; choose two or more of these to write about and show clearly what you think the author was trying to show us about life as well as the actual crisis itself. Titles to consider include *Big Brother, An Autobiography, Pratidwandi, Circus Cat Alley Cat, Roots and Shadows* and *The Only American From Our Village.*

11 The collection is full of unusual and even eccentric characters. Choose two or three from different sources and write about them and what made them interesting to you. Consider *Big Brother, Muniyakka, Pratidwandi, Master Babu, Circus Cat Alley Cat, Roots and Shadows, The Only American From Our Village, Rough Passage* and *A Horse And Two Goats.*

12 The present introduction is very informative and clear about Literature from South Asia and it is aimed at anyone who might be interested in the book. Write your own introduction to the collection specifically for your own age group; make your introduction informative and helpful but also try to encourage people of your own age to read the anthology.

13 Imagine that someone wishes to put together a collection called World Literature and they have asked you to select five or six pieces from this anthology. Choose these pieces and then explain fully and clearly why you have chosen them; you may also need to say why you have left out some of the other possible titles.

14 The countries of South Asia encompass many different languages; a number of South Asian languages, including Urdu and Punjabi, Gujerati, Hindi and Bengali, are now spoken in Britain and are taught in some of our schools. Write about the ways in which the issue of language arises in the anthology; you could consider misunderstandings; the status of different languages; the question of what language to use when and what is proper English. Passages to look at are *An Introduction, Master Babu, Across the Black Waters, A Horse and Two Goats, Rough Passage, Aranyani*. You may also find the 'General Introduction' helpful.

Sources and Further Reading

In this section I have given sources of the material used and have taken the opportunity of indicating, very briefly, some other works of interest. There are now a number of specialist bookshops importing books from the Subcontinent; Public Libraries are beginning to stock more literature in this area and there are specialist libraries such as the SOAS Library (School of Oriental and African Studies, Malet Street, London WC1E 7HP) and the Commonwealth Institute Library (Kensington High Street, London W8 6NQ).

Aranyani: Forest Spirit from *The Indian Poetic Tradition: An Anthology of Poetry from the Vedic Period to the Seventeenth Century* compiled and edited by Vatsayan and Misra (YK Publishers, Agra 1983).

Nine Tamil Poems from *The Interior Landscape: Love Poems from a Classical Tamil Anthology* translated by A. K. Ramanujan (Indiana University Press, Bloomington 1967; Peter Owen, London 1970). Ramanujan has also translated a collection of south Indian religious poems from the medieval period: *Speaking of Shiva* (Penguin 1986), and an outstanding novel *Samskara* by U. R. Anantha Murthy (Oxford University Press, Delhi 1976).

Winter, from *The Ramayana* (see above, *Aranyani: Forest Spirit*).

Last Honey from *Rabindranath Tagore: Selected Poems* translated by William Radice (Penguin 1985). Tagore's novel *Home and the World* is also available from Penguin. His short autobiography has also been translated: *My Boyhood Days*, translated by Marjorie Sykes (Viswa Bharati, Calcutta 1945), as well as novels and short story collections, for example, *The Broken Nest* translated by Mary Lago and Supriya Bari (Macmillan India, 1971).

Pather Panchali by Bibhutibhushan Banerji, translated by Clarke and Mukherji (Lokamaya Press, London 1986). The same publisher has simultaneously reissued a translation of another novel by one of the Subcontinent's outstanding prose writers in Hindi and Urdu: *Godaan* by Premchand, translated by Gordon C. Roadarmel. See also *The Chess Players* and other stories by Premchand, translated by Gurdial Singh (Orient Paperbacks, Delhi).

Arrival of the Monsoon from *Wordfall: Three Pakistani Poets* edited by Kalim Omar (Oxford University Press, Karachi 1975).

Village Without Walls by Vyankatesh Madgulkar, translated by Ram Deshmukh (Asia Publishing House, Bombay 1966).

I Left You Behind from *Take Me Home Rickshaw: Poems by contemporary poets of Bangladesh* translated and edited by Farida Majid (The Salamander Imprint 1974). Work by Dawood Haider is included in *Fifty Poems from Bangladesh* edited and translated by Kabir Chowdhury (United Writers, Calcutta 1977).

Big Brother from *A Death in Delhi: Modern Hindi Short Stories* translated and edited by Gordon C. Roadarmel (Penguin, India 1987).

An Introduction from *The Old Playhouse* by Kamala Das (Orient Longman, Delhi 1973). (Penguin, India 1987). An outstanding woman poet of the younger generation is Sujatha Bhatt who's collection *Brunizem* won the Commonwealth Poetry Prize (Carcanet, 1988). Poems and short stories by UK based women writers are contained in *The Right of Way* (The Women's Press, 1988). A novelist included in that collection is Leena Dhingra who's novel *Amritvela* is also available (Women's Press, 1988).

Muniyakka from *Truth Tales: Stories by Indian Women* edited by Kali for Women (The Women's Press, London 1987).

Across the Black Waters by Mulk Raj Anand (Jonathan Cape, London 1940; Orient Paperbacks, Delhi 1980). Other novels by Anand have been published in paperback under the same imprint, for example, *Coolie, The Village, Untouchable, Private Life of an Indian Prince.*

Untouchable (Penguin 1986). Interesting background information about the Indian troops who fought in France, and about Indian visitors to, and settlers in, Britain prior to 1947 can be found in *Ayahs, Lascars and Princes* by Rozina Visram (Pluto Press, London 1986).

Jejuri by Arun Kolatkar (Clearing House, Bombay 1976).

An Autobiography: The Story of My Experiments with Truth by M. K. Gandhi (Penguin 1985). There is a lot of fiction dealing with or touching on the Independence movement and its aftermath, for example, *Kanthapura* by Raja Rao (Orient Paperbacks 1971); *A Bend in the Ganges* by Manohar Malgongkar (Orient Paperbacks 1964); *Sunlight on a Broken Column* by Attia Hossain (Arnold-Heinemann, Delhi 1979). *Train to Pakistan* by Khushwant Singh (India Book House, Delhi 1965) deals with the events of Partition in 1947. A number of the short stories in Ranjana Ash's outstanding collection *Stories from India, Pakistan and Bangladesh* (Harrap 1980) also touch on these themes.

Pratidwandi by Sunil Gangopadhyay translated by Enakshi Chatterjee (Sangam, Bombay 1974).

Master Babu from *A Little Ado* by Kaiser Haq (Granthabibi, Dhaka). *Selected Poems of Shamsur Rahman* translated and edited by Kaiser Haq (Brac Prokashona, Dhaka 1985); this is a bilingual edition.

Circus Cat Alley Cat by Anita Desai, published in *Lets Go Home and other stories: An Anthology of Indian Short Stories in English* edited by Meenakshi Mukherji (Orient Longman, Madras 1984). A collection of short stories by Anita Desai (not containing *Circus Cat Alley Cat*) *Games at Twilight* is available from Penguin, as are a number of her novels, for example, *Fire on the Mountain, In Custody, Village by the Sea.*

Of Mothers among other things, and **Self-portrait** from *Selected Poems* by A. K. Ramanujan (Oxford University Press, Delhi 1976).

Roots and Shadows by Shashi Deshpande (Sangam, Bombay 1983).

That Long Silence (Virago, 1988). *Sunlight on a Broken Column* by Attia Hosain *(Virago 1988)* and a collection of short stories *Phoenix Fled* (Virago, 1988).

Breaking Stones from *A Season on the Earth* by Nirala, translated by David Rubin (Columbia University Press, New York 1976).

The Only American From Our Village by Arun Joshi, published in *Contemporary Indian English Short Stories* edited by Madhusudan Prasad (Sterling Books, Delhi 1983). Three other collections of short stories worth noting are *A Portrait of India* edited by Shiv Kumar (Vikas, Delhi 1983), *Modern Indian Short Stories* edited by Saros Cowasjee and Shiv Kumar (Oxford University Press, Delhi 1983) and *The Inner Courtyard: Stories by Indian Women* edited by Lakshmi Holmstrom (Virago, 1990).

A Prison Nightfall, The Twelfth Man, I Am Not That Woman from *The Penguin Book of Modern Urdu Poetry* selected and translated by Mahmood Jamal (Penguin 1986). A collection of recently published translations of one of the poets in the Penguin anthology is *A Listening Game* by Saqi Farooqi, translated and introduced by Frances Pritchett and Shamsur Rahman Faruqi (Lokamaya, London 1987). Iftikhar Arif poems are available in a dual-text edition, *The Twelfth Man* (Forest Books, 1989).

A Horse and Two Goats: Stories by R. K. Narayan (Viking Press 1970; Indian Thought Publications, Mysore 1982). Narayan's novels are published in Britain by Heinemann in hardback and some are available in paperback from Penguin, for example, *The Mān-Eater of Malgudi, Under the Banyan Tree, The Vendor of Sweets*.

Rough Passage by R. Parthasarathy (Oxford University Press, Delhi 1977). Parthasarathy is the editor of *Ten Twentieth Century Indian Poets* (Oxford University Press, Delhi 1976), an anthology with critical and biographical introductions to each poet. An important English language poet available form the same publisher is Nissim Ezekiel: *Latter-Day Psalms* by Nissim Ezekiel (Oxford University Press, Delhi 1982).

On the following pages:
South Asia: a selection of photographs

1. Rabindranath Tagore (1861–1941). Poet, novelist, playwright, educator, painter, musician, and Nobel prize-winner – Tagore was a figure of international importance. (See his poem *Last Honey* on page 23.)

2. Gandhi, the great nationalist leader, shown here resting during his tireless campaigning for Indian independence. The passage reprinted from his *Autobiography* (page 64) refers to his earlier activities in South Africa.

3. Indian soldiers, fighting on the Western Front in France during the First World War. Mulk Raj Anand's novel *Across the Black Waters* (see page 45) describes the activities of a group of such soldiers.

5. (*below right*) The Iron Pillar, now in Delhi. Originally erected by King Chandravaran in about 500 AD, and bearing inscriptions to commemorate his victories. The iron in this pillar has a purity of 99.97 per cent, and·as such represents a remarkable technological achievement.

4. Ploughing. The passage from *The Village Had No Walls* (page 26) shows what happens when a farmer is unable to plough his land.

6. A building site in Goa. Women as well as men often work on building sites – see the poem *Breaking Stones* by Nirala (page 100).

7. A Catholic Church in Goa. Society in the Indian subcontinent has always been 'multi-cultural'. The first Christian communities in India were established in the 8th century.

8. Part of an astronomical observatory, one of several constructed by the Maharajah Jai Singh of Jaipur in the early 18th Century. The instruments are remarkable for the beauty of their design as well as for their accuracy.

9. A religious procession in Mysore.

10. Musicians at a wedding procession in Dekkhan. A similar procession, in a village setting, is described in Taufiq Rafat's poem *Wedding in the Flood* (page 76).